'Admit it, you are

'No! I shall never w
a shameful bargain t
never be yours!' she
strength, ebbed and she lay quiet
beneath him.

For a moment he stared down into her lovely face,
tears brimming on the long lashes. She could not believe
it when he drew back and left her . . .

Valentina Luellen was born in London in 1938, and educated in Gloucestershire and London. She began writing at school—mainly because she loathed maths! It took her twelve years of writing before she had a book accepted, but she has now had over 40 stories published. Historical romances are her favourite to write, because she loves researching into so many different countries, learning about customs and costumes and the way people lived hundreds of years ago.

Valentina Luellen and her husband moved to Portugal six years ago when he became seriously ill. There his health began to improve and they now live in a renovated farmhouse on the 'Algarve with their 19-year-old son, 21 cats, two Portuguese dogs, and around 100 trees—almonds, olives, figs, plums, lemons and oranges—most of which they planted themselves.

THE PASSIONATE PIRATE

PIRATE

VALENTINA LUELLEN

MILLS & BOON LIMITED
15–16 BROOK'S MEWS
LONDON W1A 1DR

First published in Great Britain 1986
by Mills & Boon Limited

© Valentina Luellen

Australian copyright 1986
Philippine copyright 1986
This edition 1986

ISBN 0 263 75372 7

Set in 10 on 11½ pt Linotron Times
04–0486–72,500

Photoset by Rowland Phototypesetting Limited
Bury St Edmunds, Suffolk
Made and printed in Great Britain by
Cox & Wyman Limited, Reading

CHAPTER
ONE

THE BRIGANTINE *Sea Witch* slipped out to sea on a late afternoon tide, her sails billowing in a fresh breeze. She sat lightly in the water, despite holds well filled with rich, pungent spices, tropical fruits, and aromatic oils to perfume the ladies on the island of Jamaica. A harmless merchantman plying her trade.

Not apparent to the naked eyes of the watching islanders who had been gazing unsuspectingly at her sleek outline for the past two weeks, or to any other ship who spied her on that day, were the heavy guns, thirty in all, placed well out of sight of prying eyes, but ready for instant use. She was as well armed as the British Navy, whose ships cruising in Caribbean waters often carried up to forty guns, yet as she left the island of Belcanti behind, she had the desired appearance her captain sought—nothing more.

The crew were well relaxed after their weeks ashore in the little tropical paradise, and had made the most of the welcome afforded them, as their captain bargained for a cargo with goods from other islands and from as far afield as the mainland of the New World: bolts of bright-coloured cloth, cooking utensils, trinkets for the women. If this was an unusual occurrence, it did not show in the smiling faces of those who came to land and took full advantage of the hospitality offered by men and women alike.

The naïve people of this insignificant island set in a chain which stretched half across the Caribbean did not

often have ships of this importance call on them. She
flew a British flag; the crew were pleased to mix and
brought many gifts with them, including an abundance
of rum. Very little was demanded of them save the
normal comforts sailors looked forward to after a time at
sea, and this was readily given.

Ships were inclined to pass Belcanti by, making instead for the larger ports such as Kingston and Port
Royal in Jamaica or islands under the jurisdiction of the
country whose flag they flew. The inhabitants had grown
accustomed to watching the white sails of the French,
Dutch and Spanish ships billowing on the horizon, and
coming no nearer. The *Sea Witch* with its friendly crew
was a double blessing, too, after the terror which came
often to their shores in the shape of marauding pirate
vessels—men who came to plunder and destroy and
rape . . . not to give, or to trade.

There was a feeling that this ship was somehow different, although nothing was said, and the captain had
usually exercised the strictest control over his men. He
was a distant man—but fair. He asked no more than his
goods were worth, bartered hard, and enjoyed the
banter of the men and the celebrations afterwards when
the deal was settled. This alone set fears at rest. Having lived so long in dread of pirate attacks from the
notorious stronghold of Tortuga, as those islands grew
untouchable by the forces of law and order, and names
like Henry Morgan, Captain Death and countless others
struck terror into many hearts, it was good to find new
friends.

He was a man with a hard head, it was decided, as the
natives remembered the amount of local beverage he
could consume in one night without falling over. A
lonely man, many of the women had thought, aware that

he had not taken one of them to his bed despite the offers, for he was an attractive man despite the aloofness of his manner. It was as if he hungered for one who would be perfection in his life and would have no other in her place. He never spoke of where he came from, but he was an educated man, a rarity in those parts, who spoke both English and French fluently. The latter was the tongue of the island, which had been under French rule for the past hundred years. He had also been heard to talk in Spanish to members of his crew, which gave some a few moments of uneasiness as they recalled that the majority of the freebooters and buccaneers raiding in these waters were mainly of French or Spanish origin, with a few Englishmen who had deserted from the appalling conditions which prevailed in the British Navy. But, as the days passed, the uneasiness dispersed and he became well liked for a stranger. He had promised to return to trade again, and he was believed.

Raúl, the second-in-command of the *Sea Witch*, was a Spaniard who had sailed under many flags during the past five years, since fleeing from the reprisals of an outraged father who had found him trying to elope with his heiress daughter. He pondered the figure standing by the deck-rail for several minutes before approaching.

The captain looked as if he was in one of his thoughtful moods and he did not want to disturb him unnecessarily, but for two weeks they had lazed in the sun, drunk too much and made love to many women, and while all these things were exceedingly pleasant, they did not fill the ship's holds with booty. He had something in mind, of course—he always did—but he was sparing of his confidences, and it was only recently that Raúl had found himself growing close to the enigmatic man who had plucked him from death one night when he had foolishly

—in a drunken rage—provoked one of the Captains of the Coast.

This was the name given to the sea-captains who gathered at the island of Tortuga to share the plunder they had taken. Sober, Raúl would never have had the courage to speak to Enrico Gonzalves, let alone insult him over something as insignificant as a pearl brooch which he had been attempting to buy at a tavern auction when the other man had intervened and offered an outrageous price for it.

Raúl did not know the masked man who stepped in to save him from certain death, but he knew the name —Raven! A man who had appeared in the islands some three years before, no one knew from where. No one asked. Questions were not part of life in that rat-infested area. He was equally relaxed among the rabble in a squalid tavern with a wench on his knee as he was hob-nobbing with the gentry in Kingston, or drinking with the islanders of Belcanti as if he had been born to both their odious concoctions and their way of life. He had been a mystery to Raúl those three years ago and remained so, although a bond of friendship had developed between them. It was a closeness that went beyond the articles every man signed before setting foot aboard a ship in these waters.

'Capitán?' He hesitated, then ventured closer to the silent man in front of him who stood with arms folded over his chest, staring out across the darkening water.

'Raúl?' came the quiet answer. There was nothing in the cultured tone to indicate his place of origin. The man who swung round to face him was as dark as any Spaniard, with crisp black hair which curled into the nape of his neck above the collar of a white silk shirt. He was taller than most of his crew, over six feet—an

advantage when facing discontented men, he had found
—and broad, muscles rippling beneath the thin material
as he stretched powerful arms above his head. 'I think
we have had enough of soft living, eh, my friend? It is
time to get down to business again.'

'The men will be glad to hear it. That's what I wanted
to talk about.' Raúl's gaze momentarily swept over his
captain's well-proportioned torso and again he found
himself wondering why he had turned away so many
willing women from his bed. He had not been so selec-
tive in Tortuga or other ports of call, yet these past
weeks he seemed preoccupied and was certainly not
himself. A woman, perhaps? She would have to be
something special to hold the captain's attention.

Lean, ringless hands—which Raúl had seen hold a
baby or a small animal with great gentleness, yet which
could crush a man's wrist seemingly without effort—
came to rest on leather-clad hips. Across his broad chest
was a baldric of red silk, knotted over one hip, which
held the scabbard for his sword. A brace of pistols were
tucked into the black belt about his waist. He was deadly
with either weapon, although he gave preference to the
sword with its blade of fine Toledo steel. A veritable
devil he was, with that in his hand!

'Sail on the starboard bow!' The call rang out from the
look-out high above them and they both swivelled about
to catch sight of a sail. It was but a speck on the horizon.

Raúl was aware of the gleam which came instantly to
his captain's grey eyes. Not mere interest, he suspected.
Something far more.

'Coincidence?' he mused, and the man at his side
laughed softly.

'No, my friend. It is as I planned. The ship is the *White
Swan* bound for Tilbury, out of Kingston. I have been

kicking my heels for two long weeks waiting for her.'

'Is there a great treasure aboard that you wait so patiently for one ship?' Raúl asked, excitement growing inside him at the thought of obtaining some new priceless jewel to impress his little Jacquetta.

'Such as you have never dreamed of.'

'A treasure ship? Why did our spies not tell us about her? What will she bring?'

'This . . . particular . . . cargo . . . will not be for sale.' Raúl did not miss the pause between the words. Something really special, he decided, and personal. 'You and the crew can divide whatever you find below decks between you; I want no part of it.'

'Santa María! Tell me before I die of curiosity! Does she carry someone of great importance worth a king's ransom?'

'I am not after ransom either,' came the infuriatingly uninformative answer. 'Patience, my eager friend. All will be revealed soon enough. Slacken sail now and stay off her port bow until first light. Then we shall let her know we are here—and all your questions will be answered.'

'What do you think of this cloth, Charity? Is it not suitable for an evening dress?' Angelina asked, holding the exquisite white brocade, threaded with silver and gold, against her slender form. The material came from far-off Japan, and had been purchased in Jamaica. Business had not occupied her mind all the time, she thought, as she examined the delicate workmanship. Large green eyes stared thoughtfully at the reflection before her in the hanging mirror, and as they darkened suddenly, the woman who sat sewing beside the latticed window said quietly,

'Edgar is a lucky man! You will dazzle him when he sees you in such a beautiful gown. Let us hope it will be finished in time . . . You have left things rather late.'

Angelina did not miss the slight note of reproach in the voice of the older woman, who had been her constant companion and staunch friend through many trials and tribulations for the past two years since her beloved father had died. With a toss of her head, she flung aside the material in a manner which brought a frown to Charity's pale, lined face, and said, lifting slim shoulders,

'Would you have had me married without first settling my father's affairs? Shame on you, Charity! I thought you of all people realised what has driven me these past months.' She had been on board ship for so long that she was forgetting what life on solid earth was like.

'For all this time, we have been leading an unreal existence, and you have pushed yourself to the limit of your reserves. You are a lady—and not meant for this kind of life. Look at you!' Charity's eyes studied the figure before her with open disgust. 'Breeches and a shirt—a man's attire! Your poor father would turn in his grave if he knew what you had been about since he passed on to a better place. You! Captain of a merchant ship!'

'Nonsense! He would be pleased that I have saved his business from ruin. He loved me, Charity, I know that; but the Line was his life, and I had to save it for him. Somehow I feel sure that he knows I have been successful. Edgar understands my reasoning.'

Charity made a noise under her breath again meant to indicate disapproval, and Angelina's young face became grave at such disloyalty from one she considered almost a second mother.

At first glance, Angelina Blackthorne looked extremely fragile—a delicate blossom that might be plucked from its roots at the first strong gust of wind —but it was not so, and many men who had met her, and had sought to seduce the daughter of Rufus Blackthorne, the shipowner, had found a formidable opponent on their hands. Easily outwitting them in intelligence and the casual banter that was so normal in London society at that time, she had learned it all since becoming the betrothed of Edgar Sarandon. She did not like it, or his way of life—the incessant gambling and frequent parties in London, where he stayed for days drinking with his friends, expecting her to join in and match his enthusiasm. It was not for Angelina, but, as his prospective wife, she had to make a show. A show that left her sick at heart, wondering sometimes if Edgar loved her or the dowry she would bring him on their wedding day of a fleet of six fine sailing vessels, left to her by her father. Not to mention the business itself.

She tried not to think of it now as she looked at Charity and read something in her eyes she did not understand. Sometimes the woman could look at her so strangely, as though she were seeing someone else.

With a shake of her head, Angelina turned away and found herself staring at her reflection once again. What a sight she looked! If Edgar could see her now! For a moment she recollected the pouting mouth that so often voiced disapproval of her actions, her dress, her speech. When she vexed him, he could be most unpleasant! She was no London lady, well bred and able to mix with society, although her mother had been related to an earl of some repute and had taught her much in the few short years they had shared together before her death, along with that of Angelina's younger sister, in the terrible plague which haunted London and the counties in the year of 1665.

She had been born near Whitstable, of a middle-class family whose men had always been involved in some way with the sea. Her grandfather had been a plain fisherman, her father a self-made shipowner, whose fortunes varied over the years. At the time of his death he had been the proud and sole owner of six fine sailing vessels which roamed the high seas seeking new openings for trade and commerce. Prospects were good, and Angelina had fought for—and succeeded in maintaining —the prosperity of the firm her father had given his life to. For the past two years she had run it single-handed, much to Edgar's amusement—and at times she suspected chagrin—as he realised she was as competent as any man. Sometimes she even thought she was better at it than some! She had a level head, a good one for business, and she used it well.

Until her father moved to London and she went to take charge of the sprawling house near Chelsea and began to mix with the cream of London society—it was his wish that she find herself a husband who would look after her when ailing health eventually took him from her, for she wished only to work with him and make him proud of her, as the son he had once longed for would have done—she little realised *how* she was regarded. A country bumpkin! A fool without wit or graces! Well, she had shown them otherwise, and had seen her father's eyes shine as he listened to her carefully worded riposte to a rude or unfair comment. Her conduct had raised a few eyebrows and caused fans to flutter, but she was not one to listen to gossip about herself or anyone else!

Always quick to learn, and sometimes approaching

new ideas with an adventurous spirit that her mother had sometimes found quite alarming, she launched herself into society in a whirl of splendid dinner parties and balls. Her new wardrobe was the height of fashion, intended—as it did—to dazzle and attract attention. She learned the latest dance steps, how to walk like a lady with poise and easy grace and, most of all, how to be patient in the presence of all the simpering, bewigged fops who clamoured around her like bees to a honey-pot. She had no interest in them. She wanted to meet influential people in order to further her father's shipping interests. None of it was for her, indeed the endless whirl of gaiety often drove her near to tears, but she had promised herself he would not injure his health further. He had cared for her for over nineteen years, and now it was her turn to show him her gratitude and love, and to take the burden of responsibility from his shoulders.

She had met Edgar Sarandon at a ball, and within a week had made an agreement with him for two of the Blackthorne ships to carry cargoes for him to the islands of Jamaica and Antigua. What had begun as a business venture blossomed into a friendship. Hardly a day passed when flowers did not arrive at the house, or she did not ride with him in the Manor of Hyde. Several times she had gone to court and had the enviable pleasure of being presented to King Charles. They were seen together in all the fashionable places, the theatre in Drury Lane, in the company of the King's favourite mistress Lady Barbara Castlemaine, and at all the best soirées.

For a time, it was pleasant to be cosseted and told she was the most beautiful woman in the land. When Edgar said it, somehow it was different from all the other times she had heard it. As the weeks went by, it became the accepted thing for them to be together. Before she knew it, they had become betrothed. If her father disapproved of her choice, he never said so, yet the announcement (she had thought at the time) did not seem to bring him the satisfaction or pleasure it should have done.

Edgar was all he could have wanted in a son-in-law. The Sarandons of Cirencester in the county of Gloucestershire were known to be immensely wealthy and carried considerable influence at court. Both Edgar's parents were dead. His mother had been the daughter of a duke, his father a distinguished and courageous soldier who had been killed at the Battle of Worcester, fighting alongside the young King Charles in his attempt to regain his throne from the dictatorial Oliver Cromwell.

After her betrothal, however, Angelica came to realise that Edgar was not all he had at first appeared, and that what money he had been left had been squandered in riotous living, leaving little with which to support a wife and family. When she attempted to curb the wildness prevailing in him, he only laughed and said it was expected of him, that everyone else did it! Consequently, before she left England on the first trip, he had been forced to sell his racehorses and part with one of the town houses in an effort to satisfy his creditors.

Then her father had collapsed and died without warning three weeks before the wedding, which was to have been a grand affair with over two hundred guests. Angelina cancelled it without hesitation and returned to the gruelling task of running the shipping firm. At first Edgar seemed to understand, and was sympathetic to and tolerant of her request that they did not marry for at least six months—as patient as she was with his mounting debts and demands for loans of money from her. A series of accidents at sea, which began before her father's death and which she always suspected had hastened his end, brought chaos to her tight schedule and then pirates began to attack her ships on the way home. Again she postponed the wedding. This time he was not so patient and began to drink heavily. She found the change in him quite alarming.

Often, when in company, he was abusive towards her and accused her of loving her ships more than him. He made coarse comments about her trying to survive in a man's world and hinted that she should have allowed him to control her interests from the beginning of their relationship. Cargoes were late, men deserted. Only three ships over the past year had returned to port unscathed. And he blamed her!

Angelina's anger had grown at the continuing insults until she could bear them no longer. She was determined to prove herself to him and to the grinning apes he called friends, who now snickered and talked about her behind her back. Without a second thought, when the captain of the *White Swan* refused to sail her out of port again, she had taken over the ship herself. That had been almost eighteen months ago. Edgar had been waiting upon her return, triumphant at the profitable cargo in the holds and radiant when he congratulated her. He confessed how wrong he had been and wept upon her shoulder that very same night as he told her how he had missed her and needed her.

One final trip, she had told him, to finalise the negotiations she had already begun, and to her surprise and great relief there had been no argument. But when she came back, he told her, she must surrender all her ships, and all the resources of the Blackthorne Shipping Line would pass to him upon their wedding day. She had agreed then, softened by wine and his sweet endearments, and had even given him permission to take care of her affairs. She wanted to be on dry land again, to feel hard earth beneath her feet, wear beautiful clothes and be among civilised people. Yet the moment the cliffs of Dover had vanished from view, she once again felt exhilaration at the feel of the swaying ship beneath her, the sharp tang of the salt in her nostrils, the wind in her hair. She had been born to this . . . how could she ever give it up?

'So, Edgar understands what you have been about, does he?' Charity said, eyeing her closely. 'Is that why he had demanded that you relinquish all claims to your father's business and give him sole control?'

'He—He is right, I suppose. It is no life for a lady, certainly not the wife of Lord Sarandon.'

'The sooner you are married and have a man to run your life, the better it will be!'

'I shall not lose my independence,' Angelina declared adamantly. It was over, the whole bold, mad venture, and she must accept it. She doubted if Edgar's head for business was better than her own, but she had promised, and he would not brook another delay to their wedding plans. How she wished he might have cared for the sea a little more, had more interest in his ships and their welfare, instead of letting others run things for him. Then they could have had a honeymoon voyage in the Caribbean, and started their married life beneath the clear blue skies she had come to love, listening to the sound of the wind billowing in the sails, the soft singing of a sailor on night watch as he reminisced about the girl he had left behind to await his return. He had openly ridiculed the idea, and even Charity, her staunch ally in all matters, had been openly shocked at the suggestion.

The newly-wed couple would be expected to spend their first weeks of life together at the family home in Gloucestershire, so that Angelina could make herself known to the many villagers under Edgar's protection. And then it would be back to London, to take her place among society.

Angelina had slowly come to know, as the weeks slipped by and the *White Swan* turned once more for home, that to 'take her place' meant being among people who held no interest for her any longer. Without her father's business to occupy her mind, she dreaded the endless supper parties and dreary soirées with men and women who scrutinised her every move, hoping to find some fault in her, and who would reduce her to the level of a piece of china.

She would be totally dependent on her husband for everything, and would have nothing of her own. Yet why not? Why should she not sit back after these months of worry and accept that he wished to take care of her? Surely she could find friends of her own, more suited to her background, to entertain when other outside interests crowded in on her? And she still had the beautiful black stallion her father had bought for her nineteenth birthday, a few weeks after they arrived in London. She rode him every morning when at home, and would continue to do so. That in itself would be a relief from Edgar's wearisome friends. Perhaps, in time, she would grow accustomed to his way of life . . .

'I am as at home in clothes such as these, Charity, as I am in a ball gown,' she declared proudly, looking down at the tight-fitting breeches she wore and the white linen shirt, loosely laced across her firm young breasts. When her hair was pushed beneath a seaman's woollen cap, she could easily be taken for a young lad. She had chosen such attire because she did not consider it proper that she should parade in fine dresses before the crew. It reminded them not only of their families and loved ones thousands of miles away, but also that she was a woman, and they were not accustomed to taking orders from any female. However, once they realised her competence, her knowledge of the sea and the way of life on board ship, the attitudes of most had changed considerably. And she had an able right hand in Mr Forrester, who had sailed with her father before his retirement to the land and had continued, until the day Rufus Blackthorne died, to manage the fastest and sleekest of their ships. He had given up that position of power to accompany her on the last two voyages of the *White Swan*. In effect he was captain—but the orders came from Angelina, and all the crew knew it!

'I can look after a house and captain a ship. If I could not, I do not like to dwell on what might have happened this past year. Since our ships began to be attacked and all but the most loyal men took to deserting us, we would have had nothing but trouble. Someone—I know not who—was out to ruin Father, to deprive him of all he held sacred. Pirates are one thing, bribing and frightening off our crews is another! Well, they have failed, though they killed him in the process. One day I shall discover who was behind it all. Not all our vessels fell prey to pirates, of that I am sure. So many little incidents, accidents to men while ashore, desertions . . .' Her eyes sparked with sudden bright fire as she stared across the cabin to where Charity sewed in silence. 'My father always wanted a son. I have never told you that before, have I? A strong heir to inherit the business when he grew old. A son to marry and give him grandsons to carry on his name and the Line.'

At her words, the older woman looked up with a frown, and said sharply, 'You were his right hand, and well you know it! He taught you well. When you should have been paying attention to all those young gallants courting you, you were thinking about cargoes and new ventures for his ships. Instead of accepting all those invitations, you had your nose stuck in ledgers, assessing losses and profits. For him. Never anything for yourself!'

'As a son would have done,' Angelina retorted, in defence of her actions. She regretted none of those times, nor the past months. There had been occasions when she thought this kind of life suited her more than the one she would soon share with Edgar. 'His health was so poor, Charity. I wanted to ease his burden, to care for him as he had cared for me all these years. And then—suddenly—he was gone! Taken from me as quickly as my mother and sister with the plague four years ago. I know now how he felt at her loss.' For a moment her lips quivered as she dwelt on those painful months, the anguish of losing the closest person to her in the whole world. 'I pray I did not fail him in his last moments . . .'

'You did not! No man could have done more. I swear Lord Edgar is mad to have allowed you so much freedom this past year to gallivant about the oceans like an old sea-dog—at the risk of your very life!'

'And what would you know of "old sea-dogs"?' Angelina laughed softly, and Charity, who was a devout spinster, compressed her thin mouth and ignored the interruption.

'You will not have such freedom when you are married, young woman. You will have to conduct your-self like a lady—and no more of those . . .' She indicated Angelina's clothes with a grimace of disgust.

'No, you are right, I shall not. And I fear for the life I shall lead, Charity.'

'Nonsense! When you have a babe to rear, you will have no time for anything else but your home and your husband. It will be the making of you.'

'Yes, it is time I thought of other things. We shall begin on my evening dress tomorrow. Does that please you?'

'And about time! Still, when he sees you in such apparel, he will forgive you anything . . . even deserting him for all these months.'

There were times when Charity succeeded in making her feel as if she had done something mortally wrong, Angelina thought, quickly changing the subject to the delicate operation of cutting out the material from which they were to make the gown. The design had first been suggested by the sister of the dressmaker to Lady Castlemaine herself, but Angelina had never found what she considered suitable material to do justice to its elegance until she had reached Jamaica. Now she had. She would wear it on her very first night back in London. She would entertain all Edgar's friends, and look so ravishing that he would forgive her his lonely months of bachelorhood. It was a relief, somehow, during her spare hours to resort to something which reminded her of home—how she would soon be a wife and mother, and would probably spend most of her days sewing!

Some time later, when she went on deck for some air, she noticed a group of men clustered at the far end, who hurriedly dispersed when she appeared. Mystified, she joined Mr Forrester, who was standing by the rail, to ask quietly,

'Is anything wrong?' She had known John Forrester since she was five years old and he had bounced her on his knee and told her tales of the sea exploits he had shared with her father. She could never love him in the way she had loved her real father, but he was closer to her than anyone else. Closer even than Edgar, but then, of course, their relationship was far different. 'Do the crew have some complaint?'

'Nay, lass. You run a fair ship, and they all know what I'd do to any man who gave you trouble. It's that ship yonder on the port bow.' Angelina followed his pointing finger and saw another merchantman some distance behind. She had on full sail, and the gap between them was closing rapidly. 'She's been astern of us all morning, and now suddenly she makes a run at us. I don't like it. These are dangerous waters.'

'We are miles from that island, aren't we? Tortuga, where the pirate stronghold is? Lord Sarandon believes they are the ones responsible for all our shipping losses of late.'

'Does he, now.' John Forrester shrugged and continued to puff at the pipe between his lips. His weather-beaten face was creased into a deep frown as his gaze continued to be centred on the approaching vessel. 'Tortuga—ay, lass, that's where Morgan and his cut-throats lurk. Thieves, deserters, murderers every one of them! And him supposedly backed by the British Government. He's a pirate like all the rest—and if he's in these waters, God help us all.'

'What do you mean by supposedly backed by the British Government?' Angelina felt a flicker of uneasiness run through her. Pirates! Could it be?

'It's rumoured they gave him letters of marque to attack Spanish ships and settlements. He's done that all right these past three years. First he appointed himself "Admiral" and Commander-in-Chief of the entire naval force in Jamaica. Then he sailed off and attacked Cuba and took Porto Bello and sacked it, brutally torturing the inhabitants, so I've heard, to discover the whereabouts of their valuables. Next he laid siege to Maracaibo, and must have made himself rich on that haul —jewels, gold plate, gold coin. Now, it seems, he has a taste for the life. I've heard he does nothing to prevent his scurvy crew from ill-treating prisoners. And as for women captives, his appetite is insatiable . . .' He broke off with an oath as Angelina went pale. 'I'm sorry, lass, I didn't mean to frighten you, but it's best you know what could be out there. If it's not Morgan, it could be a dozen other equally rapacious scum. We are an easy target laden down with cargo, and slow.'

'Why are you so sure about her? She appears to be a merchantman.'

'Look at her! She's not lying low in the water like we are, but riding high, with full sail. She means to catch us—and to board us, unless I'm very much mistaken.'

'What can we do?' Angelina asked, aghast. Faced with the prospect of being boarded by ferocious pirates, her men killed, her cargo stolen, the probability of rape at the hands of men who would show her no mercy, she was appalled.

'We are too far from the islands to run for shelter. Go below, lass, and leave this to me. We'll make a fight of it, never fear. You have pistols in your cabin?'

'Two.' They had belonged to her father, and were still in the velvet-lined box in which she had presented them to him one Christmas.

'Go below and lock the cabin door. Load them and wait. If'—he paused significantly to ensure she understood the full meaning of his next words—'if the ship is taken, *you* must not be. Nor Charity. Old as she is and not the most fetching of females, she would still bring a price at the slave markets in Maracaibo.'

'I am to take my own life? Charity too?' Angelina whispered. She was not yet in her twenty-second year, in the bloom of her life and about to be married. She did not want to die! 'Surely there is another way? Ransom? Lord Sarandon will pay anything to get me back, I know it.'

'Perhaps.' There was an oddness in John Forrester's tone she did not like. Of course Edgar would come to her rescue—he loved her! 'Yes, lass, he would ransom you, but by the time he did, you will have wished yourself dead a thousand times. These water-rats pass captive women from one man to another. A pretty one will find herself in the captain's bed first, and then handed down to the crew until she's of no further use. Is that what you want? Your father would have put a pistol-ball through your head before he allowed you to be violated, and so will I if you do not have the courage. Go below—prepare yourself!'

Angelina had scarcely reached the cabin when the sound of cannon reverberated through the stillness. With a cry she flung open the door, sprang inside and locked it securely after her. Charity, dozing beside the open window, came awake with a start, and stared at her with eyes popping out of her head as Angelina went to the desk, where she sat every day to do the accounting and make up the ship's log, and took out the pair of matched pistols. She had never even touched them before. They felt heavy and cumbersome in her inexperienced hands.

'What—What *are* you doing?' the woman asked, growing quite pale, as Angelina weighed them carefully in her hands to accustom herself to the fluted butts which were inlaid in silver with her father's initials, and then raised them to point at a lamp across the room. 'Heaven preserve us! You are not going to engage in that unlady-like practice too, are you? Have you not listened to a word I have said this voyage?'

'Mr Forrester believes we are about to be attacked by pirates, Charity,' Angelina said, putting down the flint-locks and examining the leather pouches also in the case. She must find out how to load these, and quickly. More cannon-fire, nearer this time. How calm she sounded, yet her heart felt as if it was in her mouth, stifling her. 'If we are boarded . . . we must not be taken. He has said they will do terrible things to us . . . Both of us. Do you understand what I am saying?'

'Pirates!' Charity came to her feet, fully awake now, her small, wiry frame rigid with horror. 'Give me one of those. No filthy pirate is going to lay a finger on you, my child. I'll protect you with my life!'

'Dear Charity'—impulsively Angelina threw her arms about the woman and hugged her—'we shall have a pistol each, but you are to think of yourself. Mr Forrester said we could be sold—in a slave market in Maracaibo—if we are captured. I could not bear that. To . . . To belong to some strange man who expected me to . . .' She broke off, colouring profusely. Despite all the months spent in the whirl of London society, she had retained a certain naïvety which only made her more attractive, more of a challenge to the gallants who flocked around her. And to Edgar. She had been quite shocked when he had suggested that it was not fashion-able for two people to wait until they were married to go to bed together. She had never been with a man, never allowed one any liberties—and she would not, until there was a ring on her finger.

The lax morals of the court of King Charles II, the 'Merry Monarch' as he was laughingly known in his realm, were beyond description as far as she was concerned. No one ever went to a ball or a party and went home with the same escort. Women flirted openly under the very noses of their husbands. Men danced attendance on their mistresses while their wives looked on. But when the King himself was setting an 'example' with his many mistresses, it was the 'order of the day'! And as far as she could see, widely enjoyed by all. Edgar had ridiculed her virtuous stance when cajoling and sweet words had failed to get her into his bed. Then, when she threatened to break off the engagement, he ceased to pester her. She knew he had a mistress, but had told him quite firmly that he must stop seeing her once they were man and wife. She did not intend to share her husband with another woman. It was still beyond her comprehension why he had thought the notion so amusing!

'Mercy me!' Charity screamed, as the *White Swan* shuddered in the water as if she had collided with some enormous object.

'We have been hit! Dear God, he was right. They are pirates! Help me to load these pistols. Quickly, now!' Angelina ordered.

They worked in a feverish haste, conscious of the fury of the battle now beginning to rage above them. The *White Swan* was no frigate, armed to the teeth. The few cannon she carried were all on deck and, by the sound of it, being well used, but she was no match for a heavily-gunned pirate vessel. A dark shape loomed up alongside the porthole and Angelina wheeled about, her eyes widening at the sight of the ship closing with them. There were men in the rigging, swarming all over the decks like ants. Swarthy-faced men with golden earrings; negroes,

naked to the waist, brandishing swords; and a solitary
figure she saw only for a brief moment standing on the
bridge, before the two ships closed and the sound of
grappling-irons being flung aboard chilled her to the
bone.

Tall, in tight-fitting black cloth breeches and knee-
length seaboots. Hands on hips, he surveyed those about
him, occasionally shouting an order in a clear, cool
voice. She could not see his face, for it was covered by a
black mask. More than anything else, the sight of that
frightened her. What manner of man was he? Was there
some hideous scarred countenance beneath? Her fingers
tightened round the butt of the pistol she hugged against
her breast. Never would she allow herself to be taken!
Sold! Her spirit slowly broken!

The sounds from above grew terrible to hear, and she
stood with Charity in a shocked silence, listening to the
exuberant shouts of the attackers, the vibration as men
fought on the wooden decks, the clashing of steel against
steel as the crew tried valiantly to defend themselves
against overwhelming odds. She had been able to see,
from the men who came over the side of the pirate ship,
that her own crew were outnumbered three to one.
It was a massacre—and she could do nothing to stop it.

Silence! The brief battle had been a bloody one, she
feared. A few groans . . . A laugh, quickly curtailed.
Was it over? What now? Why was no one coming below
to investigate the cabins? She found herself beginning to
tremble. Minutes passed . . . Little or no noise from
above. What was going on up there? She had to see.

'No!' Charity whispered fearfully as Angelina turned
the key in the lock and eased the door open. 'They will
be waiting . . .'

'I must know what is happening . . . Mr Forrester and

the crew could all be dead . . .' And then what would be *their* fate? Cocking the flintlock, she stepped out into the passage. No one! The hatches to the upper deck were still closed! She swayed back against the wooden panelling, her legs turning to water. Dare she venture up there? She had to. The *White Swan* was *her* ship. The crew *her* responsibility. She was no coward to hide below while others died on her behalf! A captain did not shirk his responsibilities—and, in effect, that was what she had chosen to be for these last two voyages. Whatever the consequences for herself, she had to see if anyone was still alive. The pirates would have found the cargo by now and were probably dividing it among themselves; that was why it was so quiet, she reasoned, beginning to mount the steps.

She winced as one of the hatches creaked as she eased it open a fraction, but when nothing happened, she stepped out into the sunlight. The scene which met her eyes made her reel back, nausea rising in her stomach. The deck was littered with wreckage, but surprisingly few bodies. She could not tell who was who among them. The stench of blood which reached her nostrils made her turn her head away in horror. And then she saw them . . . the pirates, grouped round the companion, grinning at her! They were waiting for her! They had somehow known all along that someone was below and had baited her into showing herself. And directly in her line of vision, not two feet away, their leader, for she had no doubt that was what he was. The masked man . . . arms now folded over a broad chest as he surveyed her. The eyeholes of his mask were little more than slits, from behind which glittering eyes considered her.

'Well, lad, who else is hiding below? Tell them to come up and they'll not be harmed. If I have to send men down to fetch them, it will be a different matter.' It was a command which brooked no refusal.

Lad! For a moment Angelina was struck dumb, and then she realised that, with her hair hidden and the ill-fitting clothes she wore, he had taken her perhaps for the cabin-boy. She brought the flintlock up to point at the pirate's heart. She could not miss at this distance. If it meant her life, she would kill this inhuman monster who had so callously attacked her ship and murdered members of the crew.

'Don't be a fool, boy!' The man stepped forward, ignoring the dangerous way the pistol wavered in the young boy's hands. 'I give you my word that you will not be harmed. Besides, there is another pistol aimed at your back, and the man holding it is not known for his patience. Put it down now . . .' Behind the mask, his eyes narrowed sharply in disbelief as he saw firm rounded breasts straining against the thin fabric of the laced shirt. Boy? This was no boy!

'Then you will surely die too!' Angelina cried, her finger growing white as it tightened on the trigger. Before she knew what she was about, she had squeezed it. There was a loud report, and the masked man gave a grunt of pain and clutched at his left arm where a bright red stain showed on the white silk of his shirt. Men converged on her from both sides; she screamed and turned to run.

She heard their captain order harshly, 'Stay back . . . it's no lad. 'Tis a woman!'

But the warning came too late, as Raúl brought the butt of his pistol crashing down across the back of her skull and she toppled forward on the bloodstained deck, and lay still.

CHAPTER
TWO

DIRECTLY IN Angelina's line of sight when she opened her eyes was a brass lamp, swinging over the bed with the motion of the ship. They were under way again, but where was she? This was not her cabin! Her head was throbbing madly and she dared not try to raise it from the pillow. She stretched her fingers, and they encountered silk sheets, cool to the touch. Gingerly she turned on her side, shutting her eyes again against the pulsing in her brain. What kind of men were these to strike down a woman? She would be shown no mercy!

Her eyes widened at the comfortable surroundings she beheld. She had thought her own cabins luxurious, fitted with many little things which made life easier for herself and Charity, but this one! She lay in a double bed with velvet canopy and drapes. There was a brass-topped table with a decanter and glasses directly beside it. Closets lined a whole bulkhead, and sumptuous rugs were scattered over the floors—thick, and brightly coloured. Persian, she suspected, or from some further eastern country. Tapestries covered one stretch of bare wooden panelling.

There was a marble-topped wash-stand and washing accessories, a velvet-covered chair with a shirt tossed carelessly across the back of it. A man's shirt! With blood on it. Into her tortured vision moved a man —naked to the waist—who began to rub himself vigorously with one of the towels beside the wash-stand. His left arm was bandaged, bringing vividly to mind the loud report of the flintlock as it exploded in her hand: she had done this. What retribution would he demand from her?

She watched muscles ripple across the man's back as he straightened, flexing his injured arm, and felt the breath catch in her throat at the sight of the bronzed torso. She had never seen a man in such a state of undress before. It both embarrassed—and fascinated —her. Tall, strong, powerful . . . a man of action; she had seen that when his ship attacked hers. How she had prayed for such a man to captain her ships in England when the troubles began, but even the most loyal were reluctant to risk their lives for a mere woman. She commanded their obedience, she suspected, but not their loyalty. Not as this man would—could— command, nay demand, utter loyalty and obedience from his crew. And they would suffer the direst consequences if it were not so.

Tentatively she attempted to sit up, but the pain in her head was so agonising that she fell back with a cry. The sound brought the man wheeling about. She recoiled at the sight of the black silk mask covering his features, which brought to mind those final moments on deck amid the dead and dying crew of the *White Swan* before she had been brutally knocked unconscious. Grey eyes, like flints of steel, considered her for a moment before he crossed to the decanter and poured wine the colour of warm amber into a silver goblet encrusted with gems, and thrust it out towards her, ordering,

'Drink it, it will make you feel better.'

Angelina made no attempt to take it from him. Did he think her a fool? It was most likely drugged in order to keep her quiet until they reached the slave markets of Maracaibo, where he would parade her for sale! A tight smile tugged at the corners of his lean mouth, and he added in a mocking tone that instantly roused a spark of reaction in her,

'No, it is not doctored, Miss Blackthorne. I regret the unnecessary suffering you have been caused, but you brought it on yourself, and I did not exactly come off unscathed from your reckless play.' He touched his bandaged arm, where flecks of fresh blood already stained the clean white cloth. 'If you were not so valuable to me, I would throw you overboard. Had you succeeded in killing me, my crew would most certainly have done so—when they had finished with you.'

Angelina averted her gaze from the sunburnt chest directly before her wide eyes as she took the goblet and sipped the contents. It was several minutes before she fully absorbed his words: the realisation of the terrible fate she might have suffered—and the fact that he knew her name! She was not sure what she had expected from this pirate—certainly not a cultured voice and polite tone, and the manners of a gentleman. A rough odious creature, rude and unfeeling, would have been more to her expectations, yet he seemed quite pleasant. She dreaded to think what he might expect in return for his solicitude.

'How do you know who I am? Who are you, and why did you attack my ship?' She was inwardly quaking with fear in his presence because, for all his apparent consideration, his tall frame dominated the small cabin and towered over the bed where she lay; and his eyes continued to watch her in a most disconcerting manner. So bold as they considered her body, dwelling for several long minutes on the firm swell of her breasts before continuing down over her long slender legs, encased in the ill-fitting breeches, to the leather boots. Such intense scrutiny made her feel uneasy. She must not show him how terrified she was, she decided, gathering what little remained of her dwindling courage, and a faint glow of defiance registered in the depths of her green eyes.

'Your ship?' Above the silk mask a black eyebrow winged quizzingly as the man leaned back against one of the bedposts, his arms folded across a broad chest with its mat of dark curled hair. 'It flies the personal pennant of Edgar Sarandon. Does he employ women to sail ships for him now?'

'I am to wed Lord Sarandon upon my return to England,' Angelina returned coldly. 'The *White Swan*, and the other ships left to me by my father, will be part of my dowry to him on our wedding day.' He knew not only who she was, but had recognised the insignia! Was this the monster who had been attacking their ships, stealing their precious cargoes and causing havoc to all she had built up over the years? Oh, if only she was a man! She could take up a sword and defend herself against this cut-throat, demand recompense for the lives he had taken, the sorrow to bereaved families, and the many sleepless nights he had given her. 'How is it you know me?'

'You created quite a stir when you sailed the *White Swan* into Port Royal last year. You were the only topic of conversation for months afterwards. I made it my business to find out who you were. I found your achievement quite—fascinating. Allow me to introduce myself, so that you no longer feel at a disadvantage. I am Raven. You may call me that—if you wish—or whatever you please. However, an outburst of flowery adjectives to soothe your wounded pride will avail you naught. I am immune to rudeness: one becomes accustomed to it in these parts, and in one so young and beautiful it would be most unbecoming.'

He was laughing at her, Angelina thought, almost choking with anger at the infuriating gleam which sprang to his eyes. She had a temper to match her flame-red hair, and she did not always succeed in keeping it under control when provoked—as this man was provoking her now.

'So, you made enquiries about me—with this in mind, I suppose?' she retorted bitterly. 'The murderous attack on my ship, the deaths of innocent men—and my abduction!' She winced as the rising tide of anger in her caused her head to throb even more maddeningly.

'Had the *White Swan* not opened fire on me, there would have been no engagement. I would have merely boarded her—and taken you. There would have been little or no bloodshed. The fault lies with you, my girl, if you gave the order, or with whomever you entrusted with her command.'

Angelina caught her breath at the statement. The colour—what little there was—ebbed from her cheeks. Her! He wanted her! She shivered, and the movement brought a frown to his bronzed forehead.

'You have nothing to fear from me,' he said in a gentler tone, but she was not convinced. He was hoping she would give him no trouble while he went about making arrangements to ransom her, she thought, but when she dared to glance up into those slate-grey eyes, she felt far from secure. What was the matter with her? Many men had looked at her and wanted her, and she had treated them with the contempt they deserved. This pirate—Raven eyed her more boldly, more audaciously, than any other man—gave her the impression that if he found her attractive enough to make love to, then her unwillingness would not deter him. She felt herself grow inexplicably hot to think of being held in those strong arms, against that bare chest, subjected to the agony of his kisses. She was no more safe in his company than she would be with his motley crew!

'Where are my men? And my companion, Charity Simpkin? What have you done with them, you—you inhuman monster!'

'Miss Simpkin is in a cabin near by. Not a hair of her head has been touched, nor will it be. You have my word on it,' Raven replied, unperturbed by the momentary flash of fire in her eyes. What a woman—a prize indeed —he had not been wasting his time. She was well worth waiting for! Courage and beauty and spirit! They would all be lost on Edgar, Lord Sarandon . . . but not on him! 'Your crew are still aboard the *White Swan*, which is now under the command of one of my men who will sail her to Tortuga. Confined below decks, of course, where they can do no further mischief.' The deep voice hardened slightly, indicating displeasure at her belligerent tone.

The name struck terror into Angelina's heart. Quickly she put aside the wine so that he would not see how her hand had begun to tremble. Tortuga, the dreaded pirate stronghold—the most feared place in the Caribbean. And he was taking her there! To ransom? Or to sell? She wanted to ask, but the words stuck in her throat and she buried her head in the pillow in despair.

'You should rest after that knock on the head,' she heard him say. She could not bring herself to look up at him again. 'You were lucky that it was only a glancing blow.'

'Go away! Leave me in peace.' She would not have been so frightened had he not made it so abundantly clear that *she* had been the object of his interest for some considerable time.

'We shall talk when you are feeling better.' He moved

away from her. 'Please do nothing foolish, such as trying to leave the cabin. My men are a rough lot, and you would not like their uncouth ways. So long as you remain in here, you will be safe.'

'I want Charity. I demand that you send her to me,' she cried in a muffled tone, and heard soft laughter drift to her.

'You are in no position to demand anything, my dear child. The sooner you resign yourself to that fact, the better.'

She heard the closing of the door, a bolt being shot home on the far side. She could not leave the cabin if she tried, she thought miserably. Child, indeed! A child who could bring him a veritable fortune from Edgar Sarandon! Wearily her eyes began to close, and without wanting to, she drifted into sleep.

When she awoke, she was relieved to find that the ache in her head had gone. She felt refreshed and her energy replenished, and discovered as she sat up that her courage was also returning. Why was she so afraid of this man called Raven? She had nothing to fear from him, for she was too valuable for him to harm in any way. And that would be her weapon. She could demand to be treated with respect, to have Charity with her at all times, that her crew be freed or, at the very least, that they were well fed and enduring no hardships. She was his prisoner, but she had a strong weapon against him —his love of money! It was inconceivable that she would simply endure what was happening to her and do nothing!

However, when the sound of the bolt on the door being drawn back brought her to her feet and Raven's broad outline filled the doorway, she did not feel quite so sure of herself. And then she gave a glad cry as two seamen dragged in the brassbound chest containing her clothes and personal belongings. She had thought it long since divided among the pirate crew. Would the contents be intact? The small amount of jewels she had hidden among her underclothes at the very bottom. And what about the new bolts of Japanese cloth she had purchased in Jamaica to bring her trousseau up to date with the latest London styles? The silver-framed miniatures of her father and Edgar? None of it was worth a great deal, although the latter items were of great sentimental value to her. But to men who made a living robbing those at sea, anything would be of value, she thought, as Raven bent to throw back the lid.

'I carry nothing of importance, Captain Raven,' she said stiffly, as he examined the modest array of dresses she had brought along. None of them compared with the exquisite array of finery which rested in her closets in the house in London awaiting her return.

With a mocking glance, he held up several modest, quite plainly cut day dresses and surveyed them with a half smile.

'I had heard you like only the best, Miss Blackthorne. Edgar Sarandon would not have you appear in these,' he drawled.

Colour flooded into Angelina's pale countenance at the gibe. They were part of the wardrobe she considered suitable to wear while on board ship. Plain, uninteresting but sturdy clothes which attracted no attention. She replied tartly,

'Would you expect me to parade on deck in a ball gown, sir? I have better sense than that—and too much respect for the feelings of my men.'

'And a high opinion of yourself!' came the unflattering retort. She gasped aloud as he tossed the dresses through the open window directly beside him. Petticoats and other items followed.

She flung herself across the space between them, catching his arm with an outraged cry. 'Are you mad? Stop this at once.'

One strong lean hand coupled her wrists and held her fast at arm's length as he completed the task of emptying the chest of most of its contents, even down to the leather shoes and stockings which had seen better days. Reminders of her life in Whitstable—gone for ever, she found herself thinking as her horrified eyes followed the last item spiralling down to its watery grave. From somewhere up on deck, the sight of the drifting clothes brought guffaws of laughter from the crew. Her colour heightened still more.

Raven considered the miniatures and jewels he found with narrowed gaze, before dropping them back into the chest without comment.

'And what do you intend I should wear until I am ransomed?' she demanded haughtily, twisting against the grip in which he held her until he gave her a fierce shake, and she became still.

'You will be well provided for while you are aboard the Raven's ship,' he said with a slow smile. 'I shall have clothes sent to you, and your companion will be released so that she can prepare you to come to me later. We shall dine together, and I shall set your mind at rest about your future.'

'Dine . . . Dine with you!' Angelina ejaculated, wrenching herself free. 'I shall do no such thing! How dare you presume that I will spend more time in your odious company than I have to.'

'You will do exactly as you are told, Angelina, if you care at all for the welfare of your crew,' came the

Raven's parting shot as he left her.

When Charity came into the cabin some minutes later, she found Angelina seated on the bed, white-faced and shivering. They clung to each other, neither ashamed to cry and relieve the terrible tension which had inhibited them both since the *White Swan* had been taken.

'Are you hurt, my lamb? Has that creature touched you?' the woman whispered, holding her at arm's length to gaze into her tearful features. The girl looked as if she had been struck by a thunderbolt.

'No. But . . . Oh, Charity, I am expected to—to dine with him! I am trapped. I am a prisoner, at his beck and call. I have no choice. If I don't he has hinted that Mr Forrester and the crew will suffer. I dare not refuse, yet I cannot bear to think of being alone with him . . . He frightens me so, for all his courtesy.'

'Courteous—yes, he is that,' Charity said in an odd tone. 'I found him so, too. For a moment I was reminded of my dear . . . Now, who was it? Oh dear, so many shadows in my mind these days since the accident; I cannot remember. You shall not go to him alone—I will not allow it! I shall not leave your side. And you must eat. It would not be at all sensible to refuse food just because you don't like him. You have to think of yourself, child. Keep a cool head and your wits about you. You will come out of this unscathed, never fear.'

'Oh, Charity! You of all people to tell me to keep a cool head. You know what a temper I have,' Angelina said with a wan smile, but she knew it was sound advice. She must do or say nothing that might impede her swift release.

The clothes which arrived within the hour left her speechless—first with amazement, then with delight —and finally, as she inspected them and the jewels and toilet items accompanying them, with concern for the light in which the pirate Raven might be considering her. There was a dress of midnight blue silk, shot with silver thread and sewn with tiny seed pearls. Another of dark green velvet, heavily trimmed with gold braid, and many others each as elegant as these. Leather slippers of Moroccan leather with silver buckles. A silver-backed brush and inlaid tortoise-shell comb, and bottles containing scented oils and perfumes. Heady, sensuous perfumes, she discovered as she sniffed them. The small casket which had been set down on the bedside table contained rings and necklaces which shimmered and sparkled in the afternoon sunshine. Diamonds, huge cabochon rubies, emeralds with the deep green fire of her eyes! And ropes of flawless pearls. A fortune at her fingertips! And all stolen during his maraudings at sea, she decided, snapping the lid closed. She would not parade herself in this finery. Yet, if she did not, Charity reminded her—it would not be she who suffered.

'I hope you find everything to your satisfaction?' Raven asked, opening the door to consider her as she stood surveying the dress Charity was holding up. 'The green will go well with those fascinating green eyes. Do I have to remind you of the consequences of being foolish?' he added, as Angelina's tiny chin jutted stubbornly and her mouth compressed into a tight defiant line.

Without a word she turned her back on him and waited until he had gone before nodding acquiescence to the choice. The colour would indeed complement her eyes and the colouring of her hair. If she wore the emeralds, too, she would differ little in appearance from the way she always looked in London. She would *not* allow him to undermine her composure again! The touch of silk would restore her confidence, and the cold comfort of emeralds against her bare skin would remind her how important she was to him as a hostage. Hers was the advantage, as she had reminded herself earlier—and it was time to show him that she could not be intimidated by his mocking taunts and bold looks.

He would not dare to touch her. She tried to reassure herself as Charity helped her to dress that evening, and the tomboy she had grown accustomed to during the long voyage was once again replaced by a young woman of elegance and beauty. Edgar would not want her returned to him soiled—a used, discarded object. But if he *truly* loved her, the loss of her virginity would not matter to him. *She* would still be the same—and, after all, he had attempted on several occasions to persuade her to part with it before their wedding day. But if it came to the test of his love? Why did she doubt him so? Or was it her own emotions she did not trust? She found she was frowning fiercely at her reflection, and quickly pinched her cheeks to bring some colour to them. The richness of the green velvet accentuated her pallor, and Raven would think she was afraid of him!

Afraid? She was terrified. Her legs were trembling as she was shown into Raven's cabin, with Charity protectingly at her side. She found it was as comfortably furnished as her own. The furniture was heavy and ornately carved, with high-backed leather chairs. A typical man's domain, she found herself thinking, as she remembered her father's study which had been similarly furnished.

Beneath the window, thrown open to admit a cool breeze into the room, was a long, low table—laid as if for royalty. Muted golden candlelight from a pair of tall, silver candlesticks flickered over gold plate, goblets encrusted with gems, crystal glasses and silver eating utensils, all marked with the single letter 'R'.

She froze on the threshold, feeling as if she had suddenly stepped into another world—an alien world where she did not belong. Raven's world! Her feet sank into thick rugs scattered over the wooden floor as she stepped forward. The man who rose to greet her was as immaculately clad as any courtier she might have encountered in the high society in which she now mixed. Over white breeches of the best Spanish broadcloth he wore a brilliant white shirt, against which the bronzed skin seemed even more swarthy—those of a Spaniard perhaps—the black mask more menacing! There was a froth of lace at his throat and falling about the hand he extended towards her. As if in a dream, she gave him one of hers and he lifted it to his lips with a sudden mocking gleam springing to the narrowed grey eyes which surveyed her.

His coat, the very height of London fashion, was of deep blue, the turned back cuffs embroidered with gold thread to match the saffron-coloured lining. She had to remind herself he was no gentleman, but a pirate who had plucked her from the safety of her ship in order to extract a ransom from Edgar—and he was not to be trusted, no matter how pleasant his manner, how perfect his behaviour or appearance. It was all pretence!

Realising he was still holding her hand, she pulled it free, colour suffusing her cheeks as he smiled broadly and paid exactly the same attentions to Charity, who, despite all her misgivings, looked as if she were beginning to find him utterly charming. In fact Angelina noticed the woman gazing at him quite rudely as he motioned them to the table, pulling out a chair for first one and then the other, before seating himself at the head of it. Where else, Angelina mused. Master of all he surveyed! Well, he was not *her* master, and she would make it quite clear to him that he never would be. What was the matter with Charity, though? She was still staring at him, a strange, glazed look in her eyes. She was far away again, in that shadowy world where her memory resided; for since an accident some four years earlier, she remembered nothing of her past. Had it not been for the care and attention Edgar had lavished on her when it happened, she might well have died. Sometimes fragments returned to torment her mind: faces, like pictures from the past, but without names, without substance.

Angelina was fully prepared not to eat a mouthful, no matter what was put before her, but when the soup arrived, she took one look at the vegetables swimming in the creamy liquid, sniffed once at the appetising aroma —and took up her spoon, ignoring the silent laughter in the eyes of the man watching her.

'You are both quite comfortable, I hope?' Raven enquired, as the same seaman who had brought the soup came to clear away the empty plates. 'You have only to ask for anything you need.'

'How kind of you, sir. Then I shall ask for my freedom. You can put us both ashore at the nearest port and return my ship to me,' Angelina retorted, and a deep chuckle rose in Raven's throat.

'I am glad to see your spirit is returning. I was beginning to think that knock on the head had done away with it. Now you are more like the Angelina I have heard so much about.'

'What—What have you heard about me? she demanded, two bright spots of anger growing in her cheeks. Raven sat back in his chair and looked at her down the length of the table. Behind the mask, the grey eyes were inexplicably cold—somehow menacing.

'Yours is a success story to be envied,' he drawled. 'The story of a little girl who went to London, was fascinated by the glitter and wealth paraded before her eyes, liked what she saw and decided to do something about it. She spent lavishly on new clothes, furnishing a huge old house in Chelsea, entertaining all the right people. She cultivated only those that would be of use to her, and set her cap at Edgar Sarandon—and he, poor fool, fell for the innocent pose, the little girl charm. You deserve each other!' His last words were flung at her in a contemptuous tone. Angelina's hand went to her mouth in horror. He made her sound like a—a whore! Like one of the many women who frequented the court selling their bodies for the price of a new dress or just for the fun of it. Was he daring to suggest that her morals were as low as those women's?

'You are insulting, sir! And totally wrong in your assumptions,' she gasped.

'Assumptions? They are facts, and well you know it. Do not attempt to deceive me. You were quick enough to wear the clothes I sent you, and the jewels! You like the easy life, Angelina, with money and all it can provide. Well, you will not find yourself inconvenienced in any way while you are with me. I am rich enough to provide you with anything your heart desires. So long as you are a sensible young woman and do not provoke me, I shall do so.'

'Sen—Sensible?' Angelina stammered. She did not like the way the conversation was progressing. Something was terribly wrong, she felt, yet she did not know what, and was terribly afraid. 'I shall do nothing to jeopardise my swift release and that of Charity, of that you can be sure, if that is what you mean.'

'No, it is not,' Raven said slowly, leaning towards her across the table. 'I have no intention of ransoming you to Edgar Sarandon or anyone else. No one could pay my price. I took you from the *White Swan* for myself!'

CHAPTER
THREE

ANGELINA GASPED. She suddenly felt as if the room was growing smaller and threatening to crush the breath from her body. Raven's masked features swam before her as she tried to rise from her chair. She had to escape from this monster! It was only too clear what he intended to do with her now and why she had been treated so well, given beautiful clothes to wear, and jewellery . . . His! She would never belong to him! She would take her own life before she allowed him to touch her, to defile her body and her mind.

Raven came to his feet as she swayed perilously. With the swift, lithe movements of a jungle cat, he crossed the space between them to support her, lowering her with unexpected gentleness back into the chair.

'Leave her alone, you brute!' Charity ordered, knocking aside the hand stretched out for Angelina's goblet of wine. 'Is there no pity in that black heart? You have frightened the poor child to death.'

'No, Miss Simpkin, I regret to confess to you that there is no pity whatsoever in me—no weakness that will allow what I want to be taken from me ever again. I happen to want your charge—and I shall have her. How, is up to her, but I feel certain we shall come to some agreeable arrangement.'

The chilling reply set Angelina to trembling again. She almost screamed at the calmness with which he was discussing her. Surrender to him! Did he really believe she would do that? With a trembling hand, she reached for her wine. Charity guided the goblet to her lips, and Raven stepped back from them as he watched her drink deeply.

He had frightened her—more than he had intended. For someone whose reputation had led him to believe her morals were as lax as those of the men and women in whose company she was always seen, she was giving a very convincing impression of an innocent in fear of losing her precious virginity. Betrothed to Edgar Sarandon, she must have lost that long ago! Still, he could afford to be patient. Not too patient, as she would discover if she continued the act for too long, he mused, returning to his seat as Angelina straightened her shoulders and gazed down the table towards him, green fire beginning to smoulder in her lovely eyes. Deep green pools in which he could lose himself, he thought. He must take care, in taming the wildcat he suspected lingered not far beneath the genteel pose, not to break her spirit. It was magnificent! He knew of no other woman who had dared do what she had done these past months. Whatever her reasons, she had courage and fortitude, and he admired her for both. A woman to be reckoned with! The battle between them would be an interesting one, but Raven had no doubt that he would win.

'You seem to be labouring under the misapprehension that I . . . that you . . .' Angelina floundered for words under Raven's scrutiny. No man had ever made her feel so unsure of herself before. She had held her own among hard-talking, hard-drinking seamen, or court fops whose conversation never deviated from discussing the latest wines and their newest conquests almost in the same breath. Two totally different worlds, and she was capable in both—she had proved it. Yet here, with this pirate, she felt small and insignificant—and when he stared at her with his bold grey eyes, she was only too aware how helpless she would be against him if he chose to force her to do his bidding.

'Are you?' Raven asked quietly, and she blinked at him, not understanding the strange question.

'Am I what?' She had the strange notion that he was playing some macabre game with her: a duel of wits, or a test of strength.

'An angel. Isn't that what your name implies? Your eyes remind me of a tawny lioness. A wild creature of the night. It will be interesting to find out which is the stronger in you. Angel—or wildcat!'

The man was impossible! How could she answer such a statement? There was a certain wildness in her, but not in the way he meant. She was no adventuress!

'I hope you did not pay too much for your information, sir. It is utter fabrication,' she retorted stiffly, and the grey eyes watching her gleamed with sudden mockery. 'My father was not in good health when we moved to London after the death of my mother and sister. They were taken by the plague . . . I saw an opportunity of helping him in the running of the business as a son would have done. He had taught me much, and I had even sailed with him. Why, I was no more than fourteen when I stowed away on his ship for the first time.'

The mockery vanished, she saw, and a questioning look replaced it. Did he believe her? Why should she care; he was nothing to her!

'He always said I should have been a boy, and he was right. I love the sea as he did, although I was lucky that he did not pack me back home on the next ship. It forged a bond between us never to be broken. My poor mother thought I had taken leave of my senses, and as for my sister, she hardly spoke to me for a month after I returned home. She thought me a most unladylike person to have shipped with common seamen and the like. But I never regretted a moment of it, or the other voyages he took me on until his health forced him to retire from the sea. Even on land, I found myself drawn to the business. What . . . What you have ascribed to me is untrue. Yes, I entertained influential people . . . for him. I sought orders, and made friends with people whom I knew could help us. Why not? Should I have allowed someone less able than myself to take over when he died? Never! *He* understood. No one else was important to me.'

'Not even Edgar Sarandon?' Raven murmured sarcastically, and bright colour surged into her cheeks.

'Edgar also has been most understanding.'

'You mean you are far too headstrong for him to handle?'

'I—I did not say that. When we are married, I shall of course obey him in all things.'

'And be bored within a week! You would be craving the excitement you have known in the past, which is something he could never give you. Never fear—I shall. You and I shall sail the seas together.'

Charity gave a choked cry and began to crumple across the table, a hand over her mouth. Angelina knew at once what was the matter, and silently thanked her companion for giving her a way of escaping from the company of this odious man.

'She has *mal de mer*,' she said, gently lifting the older woman to her feet. 'I must take her back to the cabin and stay with her. It has happened before. I begged to stay at home, but she would not hear of me travelling alone with so many men.'

'Stumpy will take care of her.' Raven motioned forward the seaman who had served them so far, a craggy-faced old man somewhere in his mid-sixties, Angelina estimated. She clung stubbornly to Charity's arm. 'Our own doctor unfortunately was killed two weeks ago in a fight. Stumpy does his best as a replacement.'

'I will not relinquish her to one of your cut-throats. The poor thing is ill, can't you see that?'

'I see it is a way for you to flee my company,' came the hateful answer. 'If she is really ill, she shall have the best care. Stumpy will attend to her at once. Let him take her, Miss Blackthorne. There is no reason for our enjoyment to be spoilt, as she will be adequately cared for, I assure you. He is quite capable.'

Angelina had no choice but to hand Charity into the arms of the waiting man. He gave her a smile, revealing a perfect set of white teeth despite his considerable years.

'Don't you worry none, miss. Stumpy will take good care of the old girl. Treat her like my mother, I will.'

'See that you do,' Raven drawled, 'or you will answer to me. Not a hair of her head is to be touched. Try her with a little Madeira—I am told spinsters are particularly partial to it.'

Angelina sank back into her chair, her lips tightening. Charity was more than partial to a drop of Madeira. It was the one weakness in an otherwise flawless character —one she overlooked because of the suffering Charity had endured since the accident. A man like Raven would not be in the habit of consorting with middle-aged spinsters, yet it was almost as though he knew! She shook her head angrily. This man was unnerving her again. She must not lose her composure, or she might very well lose much more!

'Something is upsetting you?' Raven asked some while later. The later courses of dinner had been served, and they were eating mainly in silence. He provided what conversation there was, telling her to make herself at home on his ship, to ask for whatever she required, and generally trying to make her feel at ease, she suspected. It was doing the exact opposite. He spoke as though she were already his mistress, at his beck and call—his to command, without a will of her own. She would do nothing and ask for nothing—or eat nothing more until he promised to set her free. He frowned as she laid down her napkin.

'You make me uneasy,' she returned stiffly. 'I find your company detestable.'

'You will grow used to it soon enough,' he replied with a shrug of broad shoulders. 'Are you not hungry?'

The food was delicious. The meat melted in her mouth, the wine slid down her throat leaving a pleasant aftertaste, warm and mellow, but she would never let him know she was enjoying it.

'No.'

'I do hope you are not going to be difficult.' Raven poured more wine for himself, and ignoring her protests, refilled her goblet. 'If you have no thought for yourself, then surely you should consider—others.'

What did he mean? Was he intimating that he might harm Charity, or members of the crew of the *White Swan* if she did not obey him? As she blenched, Raven reached up to touch the mask obscuring his features. She caught her breath, thinking he intended to remove it and reveal himself to her, and was disappointed when his hand fell away again.

'Why do you wear that horrible thing?' she asked. 'To frighten me? It does not, you know.'

'Despite this, I am not an ogre,' Raven told her quietly. 'Although you might be more frightened if you saw what lies beneath it. It serves a purpose when we are at sea . . . My crew are the only ones who know that the face which is hidden belongs to Raven.'

Angelina shivered at his words. 'Frightened!' Her voice was shriller than she liked, but she found it difficult to control the fear now in her. 'I despise you, but I do not fear you.'

'I am glad, then, that our relationship begins on a cordial basis. Eat your food and let us have no more foolishness. I can be pleasant—or otherwise—in order to have my own way. For your own sake, do not arouse the devil in me.'

'I will not submit to you. If you take me, it will be by force. Doubtless you have taken many unwilling women in that way during your days at sea in true pirate style? Killing—plundering—raping! How proud you must be of your existence!' Attack was Angelina's only defence.

'No—as a matter of fact, I have not, and I do not intend to begin with you.' Raven swallowed his wine and again replenished the goblet. Was he going to get drunk, she wondered anxiously? She did not believe for one moment that if she refused him, he would not use force to overcome her.

As she gazed into the masked features, she tried to visualise Edgar's face to combat the threat confronting her—and was appalled that, no matter how hard she tried, Raven was uppermost in her mind. His eyes undressed her and devoured her soul; his smile mocked her show of innocence, of bravado; his very presence made her feel as if she was suffocating. He was so sure of himself, and of her! No man had ever treated her in this way—not asking or begging for her favours, but demanding them. Whatever was happening to her that she even considered him attractive, or dwelt on his strength and determination to have her? He had gone to great lengths, even risked his life, in order to steal her away from the *White Swan*. Under any other circumstances she might well have fallen into his arms, ecstatic with joy that such a man was interested in her. He was the embodiment of all her girlish dreams, before the reality of her father's business world had overshadowed all her hopes and foolish fancies.

Raven's desire for her was not a weakness. She was sure she could not turn it against him and use it as a weapon, as she might have done with other men she had known. He was his own master—soon to be hers!

She came to accept that she was feeling something other than fear—a strange kind of excitement—as he continued to look at her, his eyes contemplating her from the tip of her shining red curls piled high on the crown of her head to the milk-white shoulders laid bare by the daring neckline of the green velvet gown. Past the emeralds, which nestled in the hollow between her breasts and rose and fell with the quickened beating of her heart, to the waist so small it might well be spanned by his two hands. How many men would have gone to such lengths to have the woman they wanted? He was dangerous—and she was at his mercy. With his greater strength, he would easily overcome her. She would resist, but in the end she knew that she must submit to the inevitable. It would still be rape!

'And when you—you have satisfied your—lust for me? What then?' she challenged. 'Am I to be sold in a slave market in Maracaibo? Ransomed back to Lord Sarandon? What?' When he did not answer, a feeling of dread spread through her bones, and she found herself stuttering. 'You—You could not be so heartless as to sell me—and Charity—and my crew! For the love of heaven, spare them!'

The thought of being ogled by men with rude eyes who would prod her with dirty fingers made her grow weak again.

'Indeed I shall not sell *you*. Nor will I take money from any man for you, although I swear I shall be swamped with offers once we reach Tortuga. Morgan will consider you a great prize!' Raven chuckled. 'You don't seem to grasp your position, even now. You belong to me, and I intend to keep you. You will never see England or Edgar Sarandon again. You may not believe it now, but I have saved you from a disastrous marriage.'

'A prisoner.' Angelina said dully. Morgan—that cut-throat! Did he know him? 'That is what I am.'

'At first, perhaps, until you accept that I can give you more than Sarandon—and I can.' Raven rose to his feet and came round the table to where she sat rooted in her chair. He drew her up, stiff as a board, into his arms, gently stroking her bare skin as he did so. She shivered, but not from fear. From what?

The emotions he was beginning to arouse within the depths of her were as frightening as the thought of being forced to go to bed with him. What if she liked his touch and enjoyed his kisses? Dear heaven, she was going mad even to contemplate such things! She had held Edgar off since the first night of their betrothal, yet clasped in the arms of this pirate . . . Angelina found she could not move: she was mesmerised by the glitter in those eyes which were now as dark as storm clouds on a summer's day. Desire such as she had never seen before, passion burning like smoking embers, lurked in their depths.

A soft moan broke from her lips as he crushed them

beneath his. She felt the unleashing of the wild storm contained until this moment, no longer to be held in check because of her unwillingness, she thought in panic. Her arms hung loosely by her sides, her fingers curled into tight balls and uncurled time and time again as the minutes passed and he continued to kiss her—and touched the table, edged over it, until they encountered a knife. They curled about the handle in desperation, brought it up to plunge into his back—and she screamed as a lean hand coupled her wrist, twisted her arm behind her back, and tightened until the weapon dropped from her now nerveless grasp.

Raven held her at arm's length, brows drawn together into a fierce frown as he considered her ashen features, the green eyes wide with terror. He had been prepared for defiance and anger, but to attempt to take his life!

'While I admire your spirit, my angel, it seems I must teach you a lesson in obedience—a reminder that you are mine! A reminder that you are on board my ship and answerable to me for your actions. A reminder that your crew are in my hands still . . .'

'You are a devil!' she cried, as his free hand began to stroke her breast beneath the velvet.

'I have been called worse. Never try to do such a thing again, my sweet, or I shall forget I was brought up as a gentleman—and take what I want from you without asking.'

'You—You mean you will not . . .' Angelina floundered for words once again.

'I shall be patient—until we have left Tortuga. By then, I shall expect you to have accepted your—new life—and, with good grace, come to my bed.'

She gasped at the statement. No pretence—no coercion. Come to me, 'or else'! She felt as though she were floundering in deep waters from which she might never escape. He had said she would never see England again! Never be returned to Edgar! He did not love her—he did not even care for her except as a new toy, she suspected—there had to be another reason why he was so interested in her.

The ship gave a sudden lurch, and she was flung against his body. He caught and held her fast, and said almost amusedly, 'We are in for a storm. I hope you are a better sailor than your companion?'

'I am an excellent sailor,' she returned proudly, and the slate-grey eyes which looked down at her held a brief admiration.

'I shall enjoy having you by my side. Tomorrow you shall take the wheel, and I shall find out if you are as good as your boast.'

She closed her mind to the hand which began to caress her again. He had released her wrist, which felt as if it had been enclosed in an iron trap, and his arm now encircled her waist, pressing her against the hardness of his chest, his thighs. She could feel his manliness hard against her leg, and wondered why it did not disgust her as when Edgar had held her, whispering in her ear, suggesting they slip away to be alone together. This man would not ask . . . He would take! Was this the way she wanted it to be?

She flung back her head and stared up into the glittering eyes. 'What about the crew of the *White Swan*? You are going to sell them in Maracaibo, aren't you? And Charity—and me, for all I know! I don't believe I am to stay with you. Why should I? I am nothing!'

'You are everything, little angel. I have gone to great lengths to have you, and I shall not let you go. I have my reasons. Why do you think I shall sell the prisoners?'

'It is your way, is it not? Captain Forrester told me that that is where pirates always sell their victims. It is inhuman! You cannot! Oh, please—have you no heart? Let them go.'

'They would fetch a good price. I might even persuade some of them to join my crew to replace those lost when we engaged,' Raven returned with a shrug of his shoulders, which she took to indicate complete indifference to their plight.

Angelina's head swam with wine, with a thousand heady emotions she never knew existed, as his fingers stole along the neckline of her gown and slipped inside to scorch her bare flesh with their touch.

'An agreement, you said . . .' The words did not come from her—they could not—yet her lips were moving, betraying all she held dear in an effort to save those closest to her. She prayed that some miracle might happen to free her from the bondage into which she now committed herself. 'If . . . I do as you want, and do not resist you, will you let them all go back to England? You won't sell them?'

'You are offering yourself to me, angel?' The taunt was deliberate, but she chose to ignore it. 'You gave me the impression that I would have a much harder task in subduing you.'

'I shall never submit to you if you sell them!'

'Then I shall not. You offer an interesting proposition. I could of course starve you into submission, or beat you, or merely rape you, but none of these appeals to me. I thought I would have to go on being persuasive . . .' The breath caught in her throat as his fingers continued to stroke her skin, to caress and tease until she tingled with delight.

'You are beneath contempt! Without honour!' He

said he had been brought up as a gentleman, and she had not expected him to accept her terms. She had hoped, and prayed . . . He laughed at her indignation.

'If I were, you would not still be sleeping alone tonight. Are you a virgin, my angel, or did Edgar tumble you with the ease he has persuaded so many other beautiful women?'

'No!' Her cheeks flamed at the suggestion, and Raven's eyes narrowed at the sight of them. God's blood! Had he been wrong about her?

'He tried to make love to you, of course? You are too tempting a morsel for him to keep his hands off,' he insisted.

'There were times when he went beyond the bounds of propriety,' Angelina admitted reluctantly, and a deep chuckle rose in Raven's throat. 'But I allow no man to take liberties with me—not even him!'

'There will be no such boundaries between us. You shall have your wish. Accept me, and no harm will come to your crew, or to Charity.'

Mutely she nodded, but he wanted more. Slipping a finger beneath her chin he tilted back her head, forcing her to look at him. She inwardly quailed at the passion now blazing out of his eyes, together with something she could only think was—triumph!

'Say it! I want to hear it from those pretty lips.'

'I—I shall accept you.' It was done. She felt weak —lightheaded. A whole world was destroyed with those few words. Another was about to open up before her. Could she accept that? She would escape from him somehow. She had to, no matter what it took!

'Perhaps we should put a seal on our new relationship. It is not that I do not trust you, you understand . . .' She felt him slide the velvet away from her shoulders until her breasts were almost free of the bodice. His fingers traced their downward rise, seeking lower until she closed her eyes in an agony of suspense and terror. He kissed her very slowly, with the expertise, surely, of a man who had made love to many women. She was a child in his arms, inexperienced, unmoved by the men who had tried to make love to her and had aroused only revulsion. Edgar was the only man who had ever dared to make advances to her and not been totally rejected. She had allowed him some small leniency because they were soon to be married, but his kisses and caresses had brought disappointment and frustration. Was it her fault, she had often wondered? Would love come after they were man and wife and had grown to know each other well?

Raven's skilful fingers burned her skin like fire as he trailed kisses in the wake of his explorations, until his lips achieved their goal. She was limp in his arms, as near to fainting from pure pleasure as from fear of what was to come. The bodice fell away from her shoulders, baring her breasts to his hands and his lips, and deep within her was awakened something new and overwhelming. She found she did not want him to stop! Had it been Edgar, she would never have allowed things to go as far as this—but Raven! Could she have prevented him if she had tried? She doubted it, and she was giving herself to him in return for the lives of Charity and her crew. A small price to pay, and yet . . .

'You see, the touch of this pirate is not as terrible as you imagined,' Raven whispered. 'Did you really think I would whisk off your clothes and degrade you? Foolish child! We both know that force will not be necessary.' In his worldliness, he knew her better than she knew herself—it was humiliating!

'Not terrible? It is far worse!'

She did not realise what she had said until he drew back his head and stared down at her, a sudden gleam of understanding creeping into his eyes.

'Devil take you, woman! So I roused you after all!'

'No!' Angelina cried, and his eyes gleamed still more at the shrill note of desperation which had crept into her tone. She was as weak as a rag doll, incapable of thought, of further resistance against this monster bent on destroying her. 'Take me quickly and be done with it,' she begged. No longer could she bear this torture.

'No. I intend to make love to you very slowly and gently and with extreme care, so that your body beneath my hands is eager to be satiated, not rigid with fear. You will discover pleasure in my arms, my angel, such as you never dreamed possible. I promise you will want more.'

Quickly and deftly Raven rearranged her gown as someone knocked on the cabin door. When Stumpy entered, she was sitting in the chair where he had lowered her, still stunned by his words and floundering for an answer, and he was pouring wine for them both.

'You'd best take the wheel, Capt'n. The storm's worsening, and no one knows these waters at night like you do.'

'Except for Morgan,' Raven returned drily. 'I'll come directly I've changed my clothes. How is Miss Simpkin?'

'Sleepin' like a babe.' The man grinned in Angelina's direction, but his intended show of reassurance was lost on her. Her eyes followed Raven's every movement, wanting to scream at his control. She was fast losing hers! One more moment in his arms, and she knew she might very well have allowed him his way there and then . . . 'The Madeira did the trick . . . It took half a bottle, mind.'

Half a bottle! Charity would be intoxicated, Angelina thought in dismay. She was funny when she was tipsy, she recalled, so unlike the strait-laced spinster who was her constant companion, reminding her daily of what was expected of a lady, the future wife of Edgar, Lord Sarandon. There would be no further need for instruction. She was not to be Edgar's wife, but the mistress of this pirate, Raven! Mistress!

She shuddered as he came to her and pressed a goblet into her hand. 'Drink it and go to bed. I hope the storm doesn't keep you awake.' She watched as he pulled off his coat and went into the other room. He was moving about, whistling softly to himself, and she quickly gulped down the wine he had given her, aware of Stumpy's amused expression. Raven reappeared, tucking a dark shirt into the waistband of his heavy leather trousers. He had donned a thick leather waistcoat with gold buttons, and his seaboots. As the lamplight fell across the masked features, she caught her breath. Once again he was the pirate—no trace remained of the immaculate gentlemanly figure with when she had dined.

'I take it that I am free to return to my cabin now,' Angelina said, rising to her feet.

'By all means remain here and wait for me if you wish.' His infuriating reply brought angry colour to her cheeks. Without a word, she left him.

She stopped outside Charity's small cabin and opened the door. She desperately needed someone to talk to, and hoped that the woman was not as deeply affected by the Madeira she had drunk as had been intimated, but from across the darkened room came the soft sound of intermittent snoring, and she closed the door again, feeling very much alone. The ship rolled and lurched in the grip of a heavy swell as she made her way along to her own cabin. She was unable to lock the door, as the key had been removed, and so she curled up on the bed still fully dressed. She neither trusted Raven, not believed that he would not seek her out if the fancy took him. Wait for him, indeed! He really was convinced that she would submit willingly to him in the end—and enjoy it! What she had to do would be done out of necessity to save Charity's life and those of her crew. Never would she enjoy it!

The fury of the storm was increasing and she knew it would be useless to try and sleep, not that her present predicament was any inducement to rest. She went to the latticed window and was thrown heavily against the oak panels as the ship lurched into the teeth of the gale. Somewhere up on deck, probably at the wheel, would be Raven, battling his strength and his seamanship against the howling gale. She found it an oddly comforting thought.

Rain lashed at the windows, and the enormous white-crested waves rose and fell. It could be hours before it abated enough for her to take to her bed, Angelina realised, bracing herself to avoid being tumbled head-long against the far bulkhead. She would be better off on deck. On her own ship, she had weathered storms like this before. She was more afraid of the pirate who had captured her than of the elements!

Quickly unfastening her gown, she slipped out of it and pulled on her boy's attire which she had secreted away in the sea-chest for fear Raven might decide to throw that overboard, too. Tucking her hair securely beneath the woollen cap, she reeled out into the passage and somehow managed to negotiate the stairs which led up to the main deck.

So fierce was the wind that she had great difficulty in

opening the hatch and only just managed to slide through it before it slammed shut again. A savage gust of wind sent her lurching towards the rail, and she had a glimpse of mountainous waves towering over the ship as she caught desperately at a belaying-pin and wedged herself between some barrels lashed securely together beside her. Icy water soaked her to the skin, and made her gasp as the impact of it snatched away her breath. She had never seen a storm like this!

In front of her a cannon broke loose from its ropes and slid across the deck. Men screamed and jumped clear. One unfortunate was pinned beneath it and lay writhing in agony until the ship rolled to port, sending it crashing in the opposite direction. As men crowded around their companion, dragging him to safety, a lantern toppled from its wrought-iron pedestal and dropped at Angelina's feet. She cried out, startled, but the sound was whipped away immediately and no one heard it, or saw her crouched behind the barrels.

Where was Raven? Her eyes searched the deck, swept upwards and found him where she had suspected, behind the wheel. He stood with feet well apart, bracing himself against the roll and pitch of the ship, his hands tightly gripping the helm. Spray lashed at his face and body, tossed his hair into wild disorder, sent the cloak he wore billowing out behind him. There was no trace of fear in the proud, almost arrogant, stance, as though he were defying the sea to reach out and take him. Was there nothing he feared? Lightning illuminated the spot where he stood for a brief moment and she found herself transfixed by the sight. It was a devil ship, and the devil himself was at the helm! Why, he looked as if he was enjoying the battle!

As if drawn by some unseen force, she rose from her

sanctuary and started towards him, holding fast to the ropes which ran the length of the deck. The men were too busy to take notice of another saturated figure as they wove unsteadily to and fro past her, taking in excess sail, lashing the heavy cannons with additional ropes, carrying the injured below to Stumpy who, in his capacity as acting doctor, waited to attend them as best he could. The buffeting wind threatened to bring her to her knees more than once, but she gritted her teeth, lowered her head and struggled forward until she was standing beneath the tall, satanic figure.

'Clear that broken rigging, damn you!' The anger in his voice making itself heard above the wind—although only just—sent men scurrying to carry out the order. 'And slacken that mainsail, or she'll rip when I take her into the wind.'

The wheel spun beneath his hands. Angelina could not take her eyes off him. She knew she was a good sailor, with far more knowledge in her head than some men who had been at sea all their lives, thanks to her father and Captain Forrester, but now she knew she was watching a master at the game of survival, and suddenly felt very small and insignificant.

As he turned the *Sea Witch* into the face of the storm, a gigantic wave broke over the bows with such force that Angelina was torn from the ropes and sent sprawling across the slippery deck. Salt water almost choked her as she came up on to her knees, pushing away the wet hair which now plastered her face and shoulders. The woolly cap had completely disappeared. Gasping, sliding unsteadily, she managed to grasp at the handrail of the stairs leading to the upper deck and found Raven's eyes on her.

He wiped a hand across his face as if unable to believe

the bedraggled spectacle he saw, then shouted harshly, 'Get below, you little idiot! Do you want to go overboard?'

'I want to stay here.' As he stared down at her questioningly, she added quickly, lest he should think his company was an inducement to remain, 'Better to drown here than below.'

'Drown, angel.' She caught a glimmer of white teeth as he laughed at the idea. 'I'll not lose my ship, or you.'

Again she was struck by his total lack of fear. It enveloped her like a protective cloak, and her own receded. She became aware that he had taken one hand from the wheel and was holding it out towards her.

'Come. If you insist on staying, you'll stay with me.'

The same invisible force sent strength surging into her shaky legs, so that she was able to mount the stairs. As soon as she was close enough, he grabbed her arm and pulled her in front of him, imprisoning her between himself and the wheel.

'Are you afraid?' Raven bent to lay his lips close to her ear so that she could hear him.

'Not with you.' The words were out of her mouth before she gave them thought. Now what had made her say such a ridiculous thing? The man had abducted her; he intended to keep her purely for his own pleasure, and here she was feeling as if she belonged against the hardness of his manly frame. She was shameless! She jerked her head away as she felt his lips against her cheek.

'Look out!' A mountain of a wave was bearing down on them with such speed that she could not contain the cry of terror and spun round to bury her face against Raven's shirt.

'Hold on, she's going to hit!' He brought the wheel

hard over to avoid the terrible impact of a head-on encounter, and felt Angelina's body shudder against his as water drenched them yet again. The ship dipped violently, seemed to be falling into a bottomless abyss, and he heard her moan, thinking they were about to flounder . . .

She did not move at first, even when she felt the movement of his body against hers. He had her pinioned against the wheel, and that had succeeded to keeping her on her feet as the wave washed over them. And then she caught the rumble of laughter deep in his throat and threw back her head disbelievingly. He was laughing! The ship had almost gone to the bottom of the ocean, and he thought it amusing!

'We are almost through it now, my brave little Angelina. Another hour, and we shall be in calm waters.' Above her, Raven's eyes glittered behind the saturated mask. Now was her chance: she had only to reach up and snatch it away to discover the face of the devil who had wrenched her from her safe little world and brought her to this mad pit of hell. 'Never have I known a woman like you. We share a love of the storm, do we not? We shall have many a stormy encounter, you and I, but I shall always remember this night . . . For all your sorry-looking state, I still want you.'

He bent and crushed her wet lips beneath his, then said almost roughly, 'Now turn round and let me concentrate. In that attire, you are more distracting than the storm.'

'Then let me go below,' Angelina cried, gathering together the front of her shirt which she had just realised was gaping and revealing far more of her than she wanted the pirate to see, but he made no move to release her.

'Have you no romance in your soul, my sweet?' Raven teased. 'Have you never watched dawn break after a storm? A magnificent sight—one we shall share. Something else to remember—perhaps to tell our children.'

She shut her ears to the infuriating laughter in his voice. How she loathed him—yet at the same time she acknowledged that he excited her, aroused something wild, almost primitive, deep within her soul. If she once succumbed to this new feeling, she would be lost for ever, for she had no doubt that he would take full advantage of the weakness which, once revealed, might not be controlled. She felt neither the wetness of her clothes and the discomfort which accompanied that or the spray which still lashed her face. She was only aware of Raven's body against hers, so tightly against it that she moved when he did, bracing herself for the roll of the ship when he did.

She tried to hold herself rigid, ignoring the comfort of the solidness against which she could lean at will, but she was growing exceedingly tired. The storm had drained her, yet in all truth she would not have missed it. He was right—they did share the same love of the wild, wind-tossed sea, the black-clouded heavens where the devil rode his black stallion across flashing thunderbolts, a pack of snarling, foaming hounds at his heels. She had always laughed at the old sea legend, but tonight it had come true for her. She was in the arms of the devil, yet she did not fear him as she knew she should. She had shared danger with him and now his arms enclosed her, a safe haven from all harm. How could she surrender herself without a fight!

She would not, she affirmed defiantly, her chin jutting with stubborn determination as she stared ahead of her. The darkness was easing so that there seemed to be some kind of light ahead now; the clouds were dispersing and the rain was easing. It was over. The storm was passing, and with it would vanish this unthinkable notion that she somehow belonged here in the arms of Raven. She was tired, wet and very bedraggled. Only now was she beginning to realise what a spectacle she must look with her hair all awry, and her clothes clinging to her in the most revealing fashion . . .

'Look, Angelina, behold the dawn,' Raven said, and as if by some miracle, the wind abated so that she could hear him clearly.

The first rays of very weak sunlight were filtering through what was left of the clouds. Even these seemed to disperse as she watched, and she suddenly saw a huge expanse of pale grey sky, lightening towards the horizon until it was a misty blue. From darkness to light without her seemingly being aware of the change. Everything was growing calm: the sails billowed lustily, running before a healthy wind . . . a friendly wind, not bent on destroying the ship as it had been a few hours ago. Clouds swirled and danced. With a soft intake of breath, she lifted her head, at the same time involuntarily allowing herself to relax against Raven's chest.

One hand detached itself from the wheel to encircle her waist with a possessiveness she did not even mind at that moment, so engrossed was she in the beauty being unveiled before her fascinated eyes.

'It is a sight to remember,' she breathed, and instantly regretted her foolish words as she felt his lips caress the nape of her neck. 'But not with you. Please let me go to my cabin now. I am so tired.'

'And wet . . . And looking more like a scarecrow than a lady,' came the droll retort. He called to Raúl, who was directing operations on the lower deck, to come and take over from him.

Angelina scurried towards the stairs as if those baying hounds of hell were after her, ignoring the grin directed her way by the Spaniard. Which direction was the companion? What was the matter with her? She felt lightheaded, and her knees were shaking so much she could hardly walk. She tottered to the rail and clung to it, fighting down the urge to sink to the deck. Sleep, that was what she wanted. Only sleep.

Strong arms came about her, lifting her. She tried to protest, but the words died on her lips as she stared up into Raven's masked features. Without a word he carried her below. She lay with her head against one firm shoulder, her face partially obscured by the mass of wet hair.

How he restrained the urge to kiss those soft, inviting lips so close to his, Raven never knew. She was his for the taking. Why not? Once she realised that he was her master . . . No, that was not his way. She had courage and great will-power. To break her would only leave him with an empty shell. Deep within her he knew there was the fire which went with a woman of spirit. That was what he wanted to arouse in her. Once she acknowledged that, she would be his of her own free will, of that he was sure. Even so, as he laid her on the bed, he found himself unable to draw away from her as he knew he should.

'Where am I?' Angelina turned her head upon the silken pillow, alarm springing to her eyes.

'My cabin,' he replied quietly. 'The bed, you may not have noticed, is built in. You will sleep for hours.'

'But you said we were out of the storm,' she protested. His cabin! His bed! Dear heaven, did he intend to stay with her? She tried to move, but her limbs felt like lead. Behind his mask, Raven's eyes seemed to devour her.

'Let me make you more comfortable, and then you shall sleep.'

His fingers were at the remaining buttons of the shirt. She brushed them away, but they returned to unfasten it and draw it away from her shoulders. At the same time, he reached for a velvet robe lying across the end of the bed and slipped it about her. 'The rest you can do for yourself, while I dry myself and change.' He went into the other room and came out with a huge towel which he tossed to her, and then disappeared again. Angelina feverishly extracted herself from her wet trousers and socks. As he heard the seaboots thud to the floor, Raven reappeared. Immediately she withdrew to the far side of the bed, grasping the robe about her.

'Will you take a little brandy to warm you?' he asked, turning in the direction of the decanters on the near by table.

'No.' Her voice was hardly audible, and he turned to look back at her in amusement.

'Are you afraid that I have wicked designs on your body, Angelina? You are right. I do!'

She gasped as he advanced towards her, but could escape no further, for her back was against the bulkhead. He sat on the edge of the bed and ran a hand through the thick, black hair, where water still glistened in the lamplight. The muted light from the single wall lantern made him look less threatening, she thought.

'Can I not persuade you to be sensible and accept me willingly?' Raven murmured. His fingers rested lightly on a velvet-covered knee. She flinched as though he had struck her, and he gave a heavy sigh. 'I am no destructive demon, my sweet, just a man who desires you. Is that wrong?'

'I—I have already said that I will do whatever you want, so long as you do not harm the crew of my ship,' Angelina whispered. 'For pity's sake, take me, if you cannot contain your lust any longer.'

'Lust! My dear girl, I should have done that within the first few minutes you were aboard the *Sea Witch* if I were that kind of man.'

'What kind of man are you?' Again her tongue was running away with her. How those eyes gleamed behind the black mask, mocking her indecision, her vulnerability. Had he felt some tiny response that she herself had not been aware of? Did he think she played some game with him—as some women would have done in her position? She did not know how. She had no guile—and no experience in such matters.

'An honest one when it comes to matters of the heart. But I shall not tire you with my personal life at this moment. It will suffice to show you that you are mine and I shall keep you, come what may.'

Even as he bent towards her, a smile deepening the corners of his lean mouth, she could not move. When an arm went about her, bringing her to him, she could not move. His lips devoured hers and parted them, though she tried to keep them closed, determined to fight him as best she could. She was helpless—a victim of whatever he chose to do to her—and worst of all, more terrible than the knowledge that he might remain with her, and lay bare her body to his amorous advances, was the growing realisation that she liked his touch!

There was no hope for her. She was lost. Too tired to resist, even to protest as his hands caressed her through the robe. What was this fire which leapt within her? She fought against it, moaning softly as he pressed her back on to the bed, devastating all he touched until her senses clamoured for the final release . . . Yet, at the same time, she was engulfed with an overwhelming feeling of shame which made her cry out against the tender kisses rained upon her face and neck, and on the rise of her still damp breasts where the robe had parted beneath his searching fingers.

'Admit it, you are mine,' Raven whispered hoarsely.

'No! I shall never willingly belong to you. I have made a shameful bargain to save my crew, but my heart will never be yours!' she cried. The last of her defiance, her strength, ebbed and she lay quiet and acquiescent beneath him.

For a moment he stared down into her lovely face, tears brimming on the long lashes. She could not believe it when he drew back and left her . . .

Angelina awoke with the sound of hammering in her ears and the sounds of great activity above her on deck, as carpenters worked frantically to repair the storm damage. She was so comfortable in the great bed that she did not want to move, and then, suddenly realising where she was, she came bolt upright, clutching the velvet robe Raven had wrapped round her. It had been no dream! She was in *his* cabin. In *his* bed! Yet he had not stayed with her!

One moment a black-hearted scoundrel bent on destroying her, the next a passionate but at the same time gentle man capable of kindness. He was playing with her. She was the helpless mouse—he, the preying cat, waiting for the right moment to pounce. Yet what better opportunity could he have had than last night when she had been totally at his mercy? He could have

overcome her with ease. His kisses and caresses had
fired her blood to respond . . . No! She must not think
like that, or she would leave herself defenceless against
his devilish desires.

She had fallen into a deep sleep, racking her brains to
find a way out of her dilemma, and been forced to accept
that there was only one: to keep the bargain she had so
shamefully made. She had no means of reaching Edgar
to inform him of her plight. If she tried to bribe one of
Raven's crew, probably her money and valuables would
be taken and the man would do nothing to aid her. The
pirates had no honour either!

Perhaps in Tortuga? A vain hope. The scoundrels
there could not be trusted. Indeed the very thought of
setting foot in the pirate stronghold—even under
Raven's protection—terrified her.

As she sat wondering what to do, Stumpy announced
his arrival with a loud tattoo on the door and came in
with a tray which he set down on a brass-topped table
beside her. He did not raise an eyebrow at the sight of
her in his captain's cabin. Raven must have told him that
she was there. How many other ears had overheard his
words?

'Sleep badly, did you?' He eyed the mass of red curls
tumbling about her shoulders, and a momentary flash of
compassion passed across the leathered face. 'Not surprised after what you went through up there! Enough to
test the worth of any man, let alone a slip of a girl.'

'As a matter of fact I slept very well,' Angelina
replied, realising how hungry she was as she stared at the
food he had brought her.

'Then I won't be bringing you a spot of Madeira
tonight,' the old man chuckled. 'Did the trick for the
old girl, it did. Still sleeping, she is. Don't expect

her to surface until well after midday.'

'She—She is not an old girl,' Angelina protested angrily. 'She has a name—Charity Simpkin—and she is the sweetest, kindest person I know. Don't you dare hurt her!'

'Lord, miss, it's more than my life's worth to lay a finger on the old biddy . . . Beggin' your pardon . . . Miss Charity. The capt'n would have my hide.' He was doing his best to be nice, she realised, and some of her animosity faded as she looked down at the porcelain pot containing chocolate, and the delicate cup and saucer which accompanied it, fine enough to be served to any lady at court. There was a plate of sliced meat and wedges of bread. Enough to feed the whole crew, she thought.

'Enough for you, miss? The capt'n said to take good care of you. Anything you want . . .'

Except my freedom, Angelina sighed silently. She could not complain about her surroundings, they were luxurious; or the way her needs were anticipated: food, wine, clothes, jewels, all at her fingertips. Raven was the flaw—the dark shadow which hung threateningly over her present strange existence. She could not remain in his cabin for ever—or her own. If she did not show herself, she felt sure he would come looking for her himself or send down one of his odious men.

She would rather face him in the open than below —alone—defenceless against the inexplicable attraction she felt for him. It must be denied—no, crushed —before it took control of her totally, as it almost had last night. What was happening to her? She hated him, yet when his eyes followed her she felt a strange excitement. She loathed his touch, yet never before had a man aroused her so.

'Is everything all right, miss? You look—well, strange.'

She became aware of Stumpy staring at her in a concerned manner, and forced a smile to her stiff lips.

'Yes, thank you. Everything is very nice. Am—Am I allowed to go on deck?'

'God bless you, miss, of course. What a question, although it's chaos up there just now. You'll find your clothes are dry; I left them in your cabin. More fitting for up there than a fancy gown, if you take my meaning.'

'Yes, I do.' Angelina nodded. She would have worn them anyway. It was bad enough to have Raven ogling her, let alone his crew.

'Charity? Are you awake?' Despite what Stumpy had told her, Angelina decided to investigate the woman's condition for herself. At first she did not stir, but as Angelina quietly closed the door and crossed to the bed, she opened her eyes and stared up at the slender figure looking down at her.

'Drusilla, is that you? My dear child, what are you doing in those terrible clothes! Go and change at once before Jason sees you and has an apoplexy.'

'It isn't Drusilla, it's Angelina. Are you feeling better?'

Angelina sat on the edge of the bed and took one thin hand in hers. Drusilla again! The young, beautiful, tragic girl Charity Simpkin had cared for before Angelina came to know Edgar Sarandon. There had been many people eager to tell her of the skeleton in the Sarandon closet—Drusilla Ansley, ward of Edgar's elder brother. No one, however, seemed to have all the facts, and Edgar himself stubbornly refused to discuss the subject. When she persisted, he had grown quite irritated with her questions and stormed out of the room in a rage.

From what she had been able to piece together, the elder brother, Jason, attractive, more worldly than either Edgar or the young Drusilla, had been a much-sought-after catch, but he had paid secret attentions to his ward, much to her chagrin, for she was already in love with Edgar. However, out of respect for the way Jason Sarandon had cared for her since the death of her parents when she was but ten years old, she remained silent, hoping to appeal to his kindness and sensibility where her affections were concerned.

Jason, however, oblivious to her growing distaste for his amorous advances, attempted to make love to her one night. When she resisted, he brutally raped her. Edgar himself saw his brother leaving the room of the unfortunate girl, saw too the way he swept aside Charity, who had come to investigate the muffled screams coming from her charge's bedroom, knocking her to the floor. When she recovered, her memory was gone—and Drusilla was dead—the flame of her young life snuffed out by her attacker.

To escape the warrant issued for his arrest, Jason Sarandon had fled from their country home on a wild, stormy night, and as he rode furiously along a river bank where below him the waters seethed and boiled, far above their normal level, his horse had slipped and he had fallen in. A body, totally unrecognisable, was recovered some weeks later, and Edgar successfully applied to the courts to have his brother declared dead. He inherited the title and money, not to mention a considerable amount of land, and the whole unpleasant episode faded into oblivion.

Except for those odd times when Charity's memory

played tricks on her. Many times she had mistaken Angelina for Drusilla, and tiny snippets of information slipped out in the course of her ramblings. Edgar's great love for the dead girl, so great that he never mentioned her name to his new betrothed. How deeply her death must have affected him, Angelina had often thought. Much as she wanted to know everything about the dead girl, she no longer taxed Edgar with the subject, fearing it would be too painful—and shameful—for him to recall.

'Oh dear, my poor head.' The woman raised a trembling hand to her ashen cheeks. 'I swear I have been poisoned.'

'I fear a little too much Madeira, Charity. Stumpy gave you some for your *mal de mer*. Slightly over generously, I think,' Angelina was trying hard not to smile as she carefully tucked the covers about her. 'You must stay here and rest until you feel better. I shall come back in a little while.'

'You are not to go on deck in that—that attire, do you hear me?' Charity mumbled, her eyes already beginning to close again. 'You must stay here with me, where you are safe. By my side . . .'

'Good advice, sweet Charity,' Angelina murmured softly, 'but I must ignore it. For all our sakes.' Safe! With Raven aboard, nowhere was she safe!

Gently she kissed a pale cheek and tiptoed from the room. A soft snore followed her out through the door . . .

CHAPTER
FOUR

'Up here, Angelina!' Raven's voice sounded behind her as she came up and stood looking about her. There was not a cloud in the sky. Sea birds wheeled and circled over the ship, indicating that land was near, although she could see no sign of it.

Deliberately she lingered a moment longer before climbing the narrow steps to the afterdeck where Raven stood at the wheel. Had he been up all night, she wondered? If so, he showed no signs of fatigue. The eyes which raked her from head to toe were clear and alert. A smile deepened the corners of his mouth as she came to stand near—but not close to—him.

'Stumpy has been looking after you?' he enquired pleasantly.

'Yes, thank you,' she replied stiffly. She had no intention of allowing herself to be taken in by his cordial manner.

'I'm glad to see you have suffered no ill-effects from the storm.' Raven's gaze flickered over her flushed cheeks as he spoke. Already the wind had brought colour to them. 'Take care in this sun; it is stronger than one imagines. With your colouring, you might very well burn.'

'Your concern is most touching, but unnecessary and totally out of character,' Angelina answered, a flash of green fire lighting up her eyes. 'I am not a child, and I have sailed these waters before.'

'Ah, yes, I was forgetting you are a seasoned sea-captain. Come and take the wheel. Show me what it is—if anything—that puts you a cut above the rest of us poor sea-dogs.' There was a hard edge to Raven's voice which warned her she had gone far enough with her sarcasm. It was in her mind to refuse his challenge, but some unseen hand pushed her closer, and as he stepped back, her hands accepted the helm.

Angelina Blackthorne at the wheel of a pirate ship! Heaven forbid! Thank goodness no one could see her from the *White Swan*, or they would think she had taken leave of her senses. As indeed she must have done to have risen to his taunt—but it was too late—the ship was hers . . .

Raven folded his arms and leaned back against the mast behind him, grey eyes narrowing as he silently acknowledged her skill. She had been taught well. A slip of a girl, but strong of character, unlike the many empty-headed females he had met—and made love to—over the years. He had never met one like this!

'Bring her into the wind,' he ordered. 'I ran with the storm last night and we have come too close to the coast. I don't want to risk an encounter with a Spanish galleon with you aboard, my sweet.'

'Don't call me that.' Angelina snapped, tight-lipped, as she spun the wheel. It was a perfectly balanced helm, not as heavy as that aboard the *White Swan*. This was a ship fitted out for a man who knew much about the sea, she thought, allowing her eyes to wander along the decks. Well fitted out, scrupulously maintained by an expert crew who went about their work with the minimum of orders being shouted at them. An innocent-looking ship, until one considered the terrible cannon hidden below decks waiting to destroy some truly innocent vessel upon the high seas. Raven was a pirate, and she must not forget it. But how easy it was when she cast a sidelong glance at that hawk-like profile. She loathed him—feared him—and yet . . .

'Very well, my angel. We should reach Tortuga tomorrow. I hope you are giving some thought to our agreement,' Raven drawled. 'I shall tolerate no female hysterics once we leave port again, so I advise you, here and now, not to consider them.'

Tortuga—so soon! Of course she was giving thought to what she had promised him. How could she think of anything else? It seemed that Tortuga would be her one and only chance of escaping from his clutches.

'When—when did you—first see me?' She could contain the question no longer, and to her dismay and embarrassment, Raven threw back his head and roared with laughter. She compressed her lips and pretended to ignore the curious glances coming her way from the crew at the sight of her at the wheel. Nudges and whispers, a few smirks as the men passed to and fro below. How she hated them all!

'I was wondering how long you would be able to contain your curiosity! In Port Royal, when you came ashore from your ship. The *Sea Witch* was anchored alongside,' he replied coolly.

'You—You come and go from Port Royal unchallenged?' she gasped.

'When she is in port, she does not look as she does now—no more do I,' Raven chuckled, his smile derisive at her show of astonishment. He had been leaning over the deck-rail waiting for the arrival of Seth Courtney when he had had his first glimpse of her on that sultry July day. She was standing at the bottom of the gangplank on the cluttered quay, amid packing-cases and bulging sacks, a strong wind whipping at her skirts, tossing the flame-red hair in profusion about her shoulders as it was doing now. He had to restrain the urge to cross to where she was and run his fingers through the fiery mane, to crush her against him and possess those full, tempting lips.

She had looked like a demure Puritan maid in a simple grey gown, the severity of colour broken only by a white lace collar. He smiled as she continued to stare at him in disbelief—he knew that her curiosity was aroused, and he had hoped it would be. He knew better now. She was no fragile flower who would break in the first fierce breeze, and he was glad of it. By God, she was all woman—although, he surmised, totally unaware of her own potential despite all the rumours he had heard to the contrary—and she was his!

'The second time I saw you was three days later at the ball at the Courtney residence.' She had been exquisitely gowned then in white taffeta and silk, the shining red curls piled high and interlaced with a rope of flawless pearls. Her head had been thrown back, her eyes glowing with the deep lustre of priceless emeralds—and she had been laughing at something the man at her side had just said. It was her laughter—so clear and sparkling, yet unaffected—that drew him to the door of the study where he had been enjoying the last of a bottle of Seth Courtney's vintage brandy before returning to his ship.

By then he had learned much of her background and circumstances. It had been a shock to discover she was about to be married to Edgar Sarandon, but not for one moment did it deter him from his intent to have her for himself. In doing so, he estimated he would be saving her from an ill-fated marriage to a man who would squander all her money at the gambling-tables, betray her with countless women and subject her to fits of his ugly temper. She deserved better, and he, Raven, was the man to give it to her.

He eased himself away from the mast. Angelina froze as he came behind her, and his hands closed over hers as they rested on the wheel. His nearness was an instant reminder of the intimacy they had shared hours before.

'The moment I first saw you, I thought I must have that woman,' he whispered in her ear. She felt the warmth of his breath against her neck and then the distinct touch of his lips against her skin.

'Just like that?' she returned, angrily trying to avoid contact with his lean, hard body, but he was standing so close that it was impossible. 'Do you always get what you want so easily?'

'Easily? I spent months, and a great deal of money, to find out about you, my little angel. If it had been easy—and you, accessible—it would not have been such a challenge to me. Do I always get what I want? Usually. I have made it a way of life.'

'A selfish one!' His effrontery appalled her.

'When everything I owned was taken from me by others motivated by greed and selfishness, I learned a hard lesson. In order to live, and survive, I became as those about me. I take what I want.'

Was he trying to vindicate the way he lived: the killing and plundering? He had seen her, wanted her, and abducted her! He was a pirate—and she would see him hanged for what he had done. Somehow, some day, he would pay!

'Must you stand so close?' she said coldly, as the gentle motion of the ship brought him brushing against her, and an involuntary shiver of excitement leapt unbidden through her body.

'Why, I like the feel of you against me. You did not protest before.'

'Your men are staring at us.'

'No doubt appreciating my good fortune. Fate has been good to me.'

'Fate had nothing to do with it!' Angelina cried. Unconsciously she had begun to relax back against him. As his arms closed about her, she suddenly realised how her body was betraying her, and with a soft cry sprang away from him as if stuck with a thousand red-hot needles.

'For pity's sake, let me go! You said I have until we leave Tortuga. Must I suffer the indignity of your touch before then? Does your word mean nothing?'

Raven's arms fell away from her. As he stepped in front of the wheel, she saw his eyes blazing like hot embers.

'Be careful, very careful, that you do not allow that tongue to run away with you again. Yes, you shall have until Tortuga—but if I wish to touch you or kiss you, angel, then I shall, and you will not stop me.'

'I want to go below,' she whispered wretchedly. How foolish of her to think she could get the better of him!

She found herself beginning to tremble from head to toe. A bargain of mere words was one thing. She had made it with brave defiance, never really believing that the day would arrive when Raven would demand her submission . . . But now, contemplating the reality, the stark, ugly fact that she was expected to comply with his every desire, she was terrified.

'There is nowhere aboard this ship, or anywhere else for that matter, that you can hide from me,' Raven said cuttingly, and then, with a contemptuous shrug of his shoulders, brushed her aside and took the wheel again himself. 'Go below, then. I thought I had found myself a woman. Instead, I find I have a frightened child on my hands.'

'If—If I were a man, I would kill you,' Angelina whispered, her hands clenching at her side as she contemplated the mocking features.

The chuckle which came to his lips was derisive, crushing her momentary flash of spirit.

'But you are not . . .' He allowed his bold gaze to dwell meaningfully on the firm swell of her breasts straining against the thin fabric of her shirt.

'We have company, Capitán.' Raúl came vaulting up the steps, two at a time, to hand Raven an inlaid brass spy-glass. 'There's a ship astern of us . . . one you might recognise.'

'A Spanish galleon?' Angelina cried, her hopes rising, but to her dismay Raven shook his head as he lowered the glass. His face was suddenly wiped clean of all mockery. The eyes had grown cold and menacing. Whoever was aboard the strange ship, they were not friends.

'Salvation is not at hand,' he returned dryly. 'Even if it was a Spaniard, you would not like the way they treat their prisoners, eh, Raúl? He was a galley-slave for a year before he escaped. Show her the marks you bear.'

The young man pushed back his sleeves, and she shuddered at the mass of angry weals which still marked his dark skin.

'Apart from that, the Spanish have no reason to love the Raven. I have sunk too many of their treasure ships,' he added.

'Making yourself rich through the misfortunes of others,' she said fiercely. 'How proud you must be!'

'I sail under letters of marque, which give me licence

to attack any Spanish shipping I encounter,' Raven retorted, frowning at her.

'As Morgan has letters from the British Government. He is still a murderous pirate—as you are,' she flung back, headless of the narrowed eyes which warned her of his growing displeasure. 'Doubtless you were with him when he plundered Porto Bello and all those other settlements along this coast.'

'A very profitable venture, from what I recall,' came the cool reply, and she stepped back from him, her eyes widening in horror. With each word, he condemned himself more. Did he care nothing for all the poor souls lost at sea, the women who waited in vain for their men to return to them? 'If you meet the illustrious Captain Morgan in Tortuga, I advise you to keep a respectful tongue in your head. His temper is quick, and you would not like to see him angry.'

The wheel spun under his capable hands and the ship veered sharply about, quickly increasing in speed as her sails were filled by the strong breeze. Angelina shaded her eyes against the bright sunlight—and caught her breath. The other ship was not making for them at all, but for the slower and heavier *White Swan*. And she was almost upon them. A puff of white smoke rolled across the water, followed by the distinct echo of cannon-fire.

'Do something!' she cried. 'My ship is under attack!'

'I have every intention of "doing something",' Raven snapped. 'Go below and stay out of the way.'

'I will not.' She stood her ground as he rounded on her, an expletive exploding beneath his breath. 'That is *my* ship, and I want to see what happens to her. We have no bargain, remember, if anything happens to my crew.'

Raven's grey eyes narrowed as he considered the defiance blazing out of her face. She was no frightened

child now, but a stubborn, wilful woman. What a time
for her to show him this side of her character! Damn the
wench—she was going to give him more headaches than
Edgar   Sarandon   and   Enrico   Gonzalves   put
together . . .

'Raúl, order the men to battle-stations. If we have to
blow her out of the water, we will,' he thundered.

'And answer to the Captains of the Coast for sinking
one of our own?' Raúl asked in surprise. 'Let them have
the ship, Capitán, she carries nothing of value.'

'On the contrary, her survival is of the greatest importance,' Raven murmured. He was staring thoughtfully at the *White Swan* as he spoke, his gaze concentrated
on the tall mast from which fluttered the Blackthorne
insignia.

Why should he have changed it from Edgar's personal
pennant, which had been flying there at the time of her
capture, Angelina wondered. Was it to remind her what
was at stake if she refused his demands? She could think
of no other reason. Her attention returned to the other
vessel. She was a heavier, larger ship than either the
White Swan or the *Sea Witch*, and she felt her heart begin
to race unsteadily. If attacked, her own ship would stand
no chance. She would be free of her hateful bargain with
the captain of the *Sea Witch* if anything happened to the
White Swan, but many good men would have died in
order to release her from bondage. Or would she be
free? She had no guarantee that Raven would not still
keep her and force her to submit to him. By his own
admission, he had gone to a great deal of trouble to have
her.

Her eyes centred on his tall figure, trying to puzzle out
what manner of man lay beneath the menacing black
mask. He had said he was scarred. What kind? Did they

sear his face with red angry weals, like those marking Raúl's wrists? Had he been burned in an accident, or scarred in a duel? How would she react when he claimed her, and took off that silken covering and revealed his countenance? An involuntary shiver ran through her body, and immediately his grey eyes were upon her questioningly.

'You have nothing to fear, angel. Enrico Gonzalves is no match for me, and he knows it. Look! He has seen us. He is turning away!' He began to laugh as she stared in astonishment at the other pirate ship, which had indeed turned sharply about and was heading away from them. A cheer went up from the watching crew at battle-stations. Somehow the sound chilled her to the bone. It was as though he had wanted a fight, she thought . . . Was he so unafraid of death?

'He—He is one of you?' she faltered, and he nodded. Handing the wheel to Raúl, he stepped to her side, imprisoning her between the two hands he placed either side of her on the deck-rail.

'One of the Captains of the Coast—as I am. You would not like him . . . He takes no prisoners, except for women. It would seem that our bargain still stands?'

She nodded mutely, overcome with relief at the realisation that her ship and her crew were safe once more. What was it about this man that made him so feared among his own kind? Was he so much more terrible to be held in such awe?

'You are proud, Angelina, and I like that. Independent—and far too headstrong for your own good—but I like that, too. You must, however, accept that you now belong to me.'

'Do you really believe you can abduct a woman and force her to your will?' she demanded defiantly. 'I shall submit to you to save the lives of good men, but at the first opportunity I shall try to escape. I will not be —owned—like some ornament!'

'Then I shall ensure that you have no opportunities to leave me,' Raven answered drily. 'I am fast discovering that hunger of the heart drives a man to extremes that not even the desire for revenge can do. You are more of a woman than I ever dreamed of possessing, angel. Give it thought during our short stay ashore. There you will encounter the dregs of the Caribbean, who will feast their lecherous eyes on you and dream of ways to take you from me. None will succeed, I assure you. I have gone to far too much trouble to have you to let some gutter-rat steal you from me! But I think, after you have seen them, that you will prefer my company, odious as it may seem to you now. As a buccaneer, I rate far below Morgan and his ungodly pack of wolves. I do not have their taste for blood and murder—or rape.'

'You may conquer my body, but never my mind or my spirit!' Angelina fought against the desire to believe his words. 'Only the man I marry—my husband—will ever own all of me.'

'I shall remember that.' There was a gleam in Raven's eyes as he answered that made her uneasy. 'I hope you are not in love with Edgar Sarandon?'

'Of course I am,' she protested quickly, and saw by the twist to his mouth that he did not believe her. How many times had she doubted it herself!

'Then you will have to forget him; he is not worthy of you. Somehow I do not think you know what love really is. If you had, you would not have delayed your wedding day for so long.'

'It was necessary.' She rose at once to the taunt. 'I have told you of the misfortunes which befell us before my father became ill and died . . . A son would have done no less for him . . .' Her eyes grew suddenly accusing as she stared up into the dark face close to hers. 'You know what happened to our ships, don't you? Your pirate friends almost succeeded in wrecking all my father's years of hard work—and mine—but they didn't win in the end. I wouldn't let them! And you are one of them. Why do you want to destroy us—all of us? Father—Edgar—me?'

'Us?' Raven queried, one black eyebrow rising at the accusation. 'I'll blow any ship I see with the Sarandon pennant out of the water without a qualm, but not yours. You can thank Enrico Gonzalves for that. He's given me proof of what I suspected, by going for the *White Swan*. I ran up your pennant. He would never have shown himself otherwise.'

'I don't believe you!'

'Why should I lie? I make no secret of the fact that I would like to see Sarandon at the end of a rope, and failing that, I intend to ruin his business. But I have no quarrel with you.'

'What has Edgar ever done to you?' Angelina whispered, afraid at the coldness which had crept into his tone. 'Why do you hate him?'

'Have you ever asked yourself who gains by the loss of your cargoes and these constant attacks on your ships?' Raven ignored her question, posing one of his own instead.

'Gains?' For a moment the supposition behind his words did not penetrate her troubled mind, and then she grew quite pale. 'No one . . .'

'Were you not about to marry Sarandon, and upon your wedding day present to him not only all your ships, but the handling of the business also?' he asked, and she gasped aloud. Was there nothing he did not know about her? She had told him of her dowry, but not the rest. 'He would have what he wanted. Power once again, money to replenish his own dwindling resources, and a beautiful wife. None of it would have lasted very long. The money would have been gambled away, the ships sold, or supposedly sunk at sea, and the cargoes disposed of elsewhere for higher profits. And you—you would have found yourself used and probably abandoned. Sarandon's fancies are short lived.'

'Are you trying to tell me Edgar has been attempting to ruin my father's business—and me?' She gave a hollow laugh. 'Why has he waited so long to marry me, then? He could have found someone richer, but he didn't, because he loves me. Something you know nothing of!'

'On the contrary, he loves what the marriage would bring him. You do not think he has been faithful to you while you are away?' His mockery stung her because she knew Edgar had not, and she felt hot tears of frustration rise to her eyes. She tried to push past him, but he refused to move, and she began to pound against his chest with tightly clenched fists, her temper rising.

'Let me go, you beast! You liar! I shall not listen if you malign the good name of a kind and generous man!' She did not realise how beautiful she looked, her cheeks flamed with colour, her emerald eyes flashing. One balled fist thudded into his arm against the wound she had recently inflicted, breaking the momentary spell she was weaving.

With an oath, he caught her wrists in his hands and held them fast. 'One day I shall tell you all about your kind and generous man . . .' he began. For a moment she thought he would say more, but his lips compressed into a tight angry line for a long while, and when he spoke again he had composed himself and was once more mocking her, laughing at her for her continued show of defiance. 'After Tortuga, I shall show you the pleasures of love, my sweet. In my arms, you will forget that Edgar Sarandon ever existed.'

The ship had already dropped anchor when Angelina awoke the next morning, with the *White Swan* alongside. She dressed in indignant haste when she saw the cargo from the latter being carried ashore, only to discover that the door of her cabin was locked. No amount of hammering on it brought a response from above. Not content with abducting her, Raven was going to sell her cargo! All her months of hard work, the long weeks at sea, her careful negotiations—all for him to profit from!

Spent from her vain efforts to attract attention, she curled up miserably on the window seat, her head in her hands to watch the fruits of her labour disappearing before her eyes. If only she had a pistol—she would take better aim the next time, and risk the consequences. Not for one moment did she believe his crew would dispose of her as he had suggested. She was worth a ransom to them! Surely there would be some men aboard—greedy men—who would help her to escape in return for Edgar's gratitude?

From time to time she could hear Raven's voice. He rarely raised it, she noticed. His orders were given in such authoritive tones that it was not necessary, and once again she found herself growing curious about the background of the masked man who sought to subject her to his will. If she believed the worst of him, he was a ruthless pirate with no thought for the lives or welfare of others who sailed the seas and fell victim to his deadly guns. Yet he had not really touched her. She did not understand him. If, as he stated, she had cost him a great deal of time and money, why was he so patient—acting like a gentleman instead of the thieving rogue she knew he really was? Why should he care if she resisted him, and caused him to use force? Doubtless he had done so many other times with unfortunate women captives. Had Captain Forrester not told her that no woman's virtue was safe at the hands of such men? When he had satisfied his lust, she was certain that she would be discarded without a second thought.

She had lain awake for some considerable time in the night, puzzling over the conversation which had passed between them earlier. Edgar never discussed his business dealings with her, but she suspected that some of them came very close to breaking the law. It had been hinted, by someone not friendly towards her betrothed, that he even engaged in slavery, allowing a select few of his ships to raid along the African coast, selling the unfortunate black prisoners in the New World. Like all the other rumours and hints she had heard about him, she chose either to dismiss or to ignore this. She had discovered for herself that it was not always easy to keep to the letter of the law when running a business, and had herself lost several contracts when she first took over her father's affairs because she would not sink to unscrupulous methods of trading—such as saving money on new equipment badly needed for the safety of a ship, or skimping on the rations for the crews as so many owners often did, bringing hardship to and earning hatred from the men who worked for them. What if he did bend the laws a little? He was no evil pirate—no abductor of women! Raven was!

As the key turned noisily in the lock, she turned,

prepared to do battle, but it was not he who entered, but Charity, carrying a tray, and, behind her, Stumpy. Rather a different man from the one she had first encountered, Angelina thought as he ushered in her companion with a smile. Quickly coming in himself, he pulled up a small table where she could deposit what she was holding.

'Is there anything else I can do for you, Miss Charity?' Angelina blinked at the mildness of his tone. Why, he was quite respectful. What had Charity done to him?

'Nothing, you odious little man, except to go away and leave us alone. Young ladies of Miss Blackthorne's standing do not eat their breakfast while they are being gawked at by lunkheads like you. Yes, there is something you can do . . .' Charity added, as the man turned away without a word. 'If you wish to come within a league of either of us again, take a bath at once.'

As the door closed behind him, Angelina found her face breaking into a smile of pure delight. Charity's *mal de mer* notwithstanding, she was in command of herself again—and of Stumpy!

'You were wonderful, Charity,' she laughed. 'How have you managed it? He is polite to me, but he doesn't jump as he does when you speak to him. How have you done it? Raven has set him to watch you, yet you have him eating out of your hand like a lap-dog.'

'My father, God rest his stony heart, was one of Oliver Cromwell's best officers. He brought me up to fear nothing and no man, although over the years I have not been able to follow his advice on all occasions. However, I feel if I were to allow that—that hideous little monster to dominate me, I should never be able to hold up my head again. Besides,' she added, a strange twinkle creeping into her eyes, 'I rather like dominating! He's so frightened that I will shout at him that he hardly ever spies on me now. I had hoped I could somehow get the key and free you, and we might slip ashore while all this hub-bub is going on, but that captain—that pirate—he has eyes in the back of his head! Wherever I go, *he* sees me.'

'Bless you, Charity, but I fear there is nothing you can do for me,' Angelina returned with a shrug. 'He says he is taking me ashore when he lands. And afterwards . . . I shall not be going back to England with you. He intends me to stay with him—until he finds another.'

Charity almost dropped the tea-cup she was holding out. 'Stay? What does a man like him want with a young lady like you?'

'Charity—even you are not too old to know that! He has made it horribly clear that I am to be his mistress. He has allowed me a little time to accept the situation, and then . . .' Angelina pushed away her cup with an angry frown. 'Damn him! Who does he think he is?'

'Angelina—such language!'

'Blame it on the months I have spent at sea. Months I have worked hard to keep father's business going and to improve it . . . Now he is taking it all away from me.' It did not occur to her, in those moments, that when she married Edgar Sarandon, it would have been equally taken from her. 'Why am I allowing this to happen to me! I will not sit idly by and wait for some strange man to come and assert his authority over me! I am too independent for that. We *must* do something, Charity, together —but what?'

Her gaze wandered slowly around as if in search of the answer, but there was nothing in the comfortably furnished cabin to offer the slightest hope of an escape. And then, through the window, she saw her ship.

'If only we could reach the *White Swan*, free our men, and sail her out of here ourselves! The cargo has been taken off, and she is light. Although she is not as fast as Raven's ship, we could make good time if we are not discovered too soon.' A smile of hope showed on her face as she pondered the wild idea. Why not? Freedom! A chance to see the man called Raven dangling from a rope at Hangman's Wharf! As soon as she was safe, she would inform the authorities, tell them everything she knew—and pray for his capture. His mistress, indeed! He would discover that she was no weak woman to go meekly to his bed!

'You say this man Stumpy does not watch you all the time now . . .' An idea was beginning to form in her brain—so daring, so outrageous in what it would demand of her, that for a moment, but a moment only, she felt quite afraid and yet at the same time exhilarated, for if it succeeded, she would be free of Raven, and really safe! From his devious intentions, his domination, and her own weakening resolve to withstand his advances. 'That could be our answer!' She refused to consider the consequences should they be apprehended. 'If I can get Raven to let me stay on board, with you, and that old man to guard us. No! He wants to drag me ashore and show me off to his friends, to parade me before those —those pirates! How dare he think to degrade me in such a fashion, as though I were already his property! If only I knew something about him, something I could use. Charity, is he still on deck?'

She turned from the window with a nod. 'I can hear him above us. Angelina, what are you about?'

'I am going to look in his cabin. You must come with me, and stay outside the door to warn me if anyone approaches.'

Angelina ignored the look of absolute horror that crossed Charity's face. It had to be done if she was to find some weapon against Raven—some weak link in his armour. He was no deserter from some English naval ship, of that she was sure. Neither was he a man sailing the seas merely for profit—or pleasure. There was something more—a deep, dark secret he harboured —and if she knew what it was, she might have some slight advantage over him. He had the manner and speech of a gentleman—when he chose—and that intrigued her. Where did he come from, what had driven him to this hideous way of life? As she cautiously made her way to his cabin, she found herself wondering what motive drove her. The need to find a weapon against him—or a desire to know the man behind the mask? It was a question to which she did not have an answer. She quietly opened the door of Raven's cabin and, leaving Charity in the corridor outside, slipped into the empty room.

His presence was everywhere: in the clothes tossed over a chair, the maps spread out across the huge desk, the half-empty glass of wine beside them. It was as though he was in the cabin with her, his eyes boring into her back as she quickly began to search through his sea-chest, hoping that the contents would yield some information. Clothes—elegant clothes in the latest fashions, tidily folded. Her fingers lingered on a lace ruff for a moment, as she imagined it at his dark throat, and were swiftly withdrawn as she visualised his face coming close to hers and the gleam in those devil's eyes.

Nothing! Nothing to tell her about him. No personal items to give her any key to his identity. With growing frustration she turned to the drawers of the desk. They were full of papers, but she understood none of them, for they were in a strange language. One drawer was locked. Frantically she looked around for something to prise it open, seized a paper-knife, and attempted to force it. It refused to give, despite her efforts. With an exasperated cry she flung herself into the padded leather chair, her eyes roving the room. In a picture of a rather bare landscape, the tall trees portrayed there had been stripped by the fury of the wind, leaving long, gnarled branches to reach out over stony ground. Withered, dying, forgotten—uncared for, she thought.

Various weapons hung on the oak panels to remind her of the more gruesome aspect of Raven's profession, several more pictures, again landscapes, although not as austere as the first, but nothing to tell her what she wanted. Was he an enigma never to be deciphered?

She suddenly noticed that the door to the adjoining room was slightly ajar. Hesitating for a moment only, she rose and crossed the wooden floor. It was a small cabin, used both as a bedroom and a dressing-room she saw from the open closets which revealed many types of clothes. Heavy, thick jackets, linen shirts and tall, thigh-length boots ranged alongside silk shirts, immaculate breeches in broadcloth, buckskin, soft leather dyed to match the brocade jackets and waistcoats. A man of taste for a privateer, she mused, her fingers caressing the smooth silk of a close-cut coat with a beautiful peacock-blue lining. Raven dressed well. He would live equally well, she suspected, enjoying the best wines, the finest foods, carriages drawn by high-stepping horses, the company of attractive women. He intended her to be a part of that life, isolated from the world of decent people.

Angrily she drew back, pushing the door to and turning her attention to the room itself. Did he already have a mistress, someone waiting for him when he reached land? Whatever he had said to the contrary, Angelina refused to believe it was possible that she meant more to him than all the other women he had abducted and made love to.

The bed was large and canopied, as was the one in which she slept. She caught her breath as she saw that the sheets and coverlet, and pillowcases too, were monogrammed with the single letter 'R' in dark grey silk. On a table beside it were several rings, flung carelessly down, perhaps the night before, and the pistols which had been taken from her. Instinctively she reached for one, then withdrew quickly, leaving it untouched. Raven must not know she had been in his cabin.

It was hopeless. She had found nothing. One last look around as she reached the outer door, still searching . . . and it was then that she noticed the sword suspended directly over it. Her attention was drawn to the ornate engraving on the hilt and blade. As she peered closer, she could make out the words, although they were faint from age—and use? She shuddered to think that it had belonged to some other pirate who had wielded it to take the lives of innocent seamen.

'*Quo fata vocant.*' Latin had not been her strong subject, despite her teacher's long hours of instruction. Charity, however, excelled in comprehension of the ancient tongue.

'Angelina . . .' A frantic whisper from outside as she began to ease the door open, and the sword was forgotten. 'Someone is coming.'

When Raven appeared at the bottom of the stairs, she was just closing the door of her cabin as if she had only then emerged.

'I was coming to tell you to change into your boy's clothes and join me on deck in an hour. We are going ashore.' He noted her flushed cheeks, and that she started, and avoided his gaze. Why did she look so guilty? What scheme was taking shape in her mind now?

She had not yet attempted to bribe his loyal Raúl, or the rest of his crew, whom he knew would not have the same scruples. They would take what she offered— perhaps more—and then sell her to the highest bidder.

'I—I cannot . . .' Angelina stammered. What was the matter with her, trembling like this before him? If she did not control herself, he would guess that she was up to something. 'Charity is not well.'

'She was perfectly fit when Stumpy saw her not an hour ago,' Raven returned. Stepping forward, he opened her cabin door and propelled her firmly inside. Charity sat in a chair, her head in her hands, and for a moment he gazed at the downbent head before speaking. '*Mal de mer* is not a usual occurrence when a ship is at anchor.'

'The slightest motion makes her feel sick,' Angelina protested. 'I refuse to leave her.'

'You will come willingly, or I shall dress you myself and have you taken ashore bound and gagged,' came the frightening reply, and she tottered backwards, seeking the back of Charity's chair for support.

'You monster! I believe you would!' Her face suddenly crumpled, and huge tears glistened in the depths of her eyes, turning them into shimmering pools of misery. 'You cannot! Oh, please do not make me go ashore with you . . . I would die! All those dreadful men leering at me, and undressing me, as you do.' A dark brow arched at her words but he did not interrupt, and Angelina took heart from his silence. 'Why do you want to humiliate me before them all? Why can I not stay aboard with Charity? Get men to guard us. I don't care, so long as I don't have to—to be shown off to your hateful friends . . . You are no gentleman to put me through such a degrading experience!'

'Far from trying to degrade you, my only intention is to ensure that you are safe. By my side, always in my sight, I should have no worry on that score,' Raven replied at length. 'Come now, dress yourself.'

'Do you have no heart?' Angelina whispered. He frowned at her fiercely, and she went to the sea-chest and pulled out the now familiar shirt and breeches. Her fingers trembled as she reached for the fastenings of her dress. 'I give you my word I will make no trouble. Lock us in here . . . leave a dozen men to guard us.' The dress fell away from her creamy shoulders. She clutched it against her breasts as Charity raised horrified eyes to watch her performance. A single tear slid down over one ashen cheek.

'A woman's word means nothing to me . . .' Raven's tone was harsh, his eyes smouldering as he considered the agitated girl before him, and watched the pale blue dress slide to the floor about her feet. She stood before him in a thin chemise which did nothing to hide the untold promises of the soft curves beneath. Charity gave a cry and covered her eyes again.

Angelina did not know whether she was acting or was genuinely distressed at the scene being staged before her. She, herself, never knew she possessed such boldness. To stand half-naked before a man and allow his burning gaze to devour her. He wanted to touch her, she could see it in his face. She steeled herself not to flinch as he stepped forward and tipped back her head with a single finger, and curbed the urge to rip away the hated mask.

'Do you think I don't know what you will do the moment my back is turned? Not all my crew are as trusting as Raúl.'

'Then drag me with you . . . I shall die of shame!' Angelina whispered brokenly, another tear finding its way pitifully down her cheek. Raven brushed it away with an oath. 'I will not break my word. I shall not leave this cabin until you return. I swear it, Raven. No, you will not believe me. You act like a gentleman—you have fine manners and you seek to impress me with your fine words—but you are not. A real gentleman has breeding; he accepts that when a lady gives her word, she does not break it. But then I suppose you have never met one before.'

Raven swore again, and she winced at the crudeness of the oath. He wheeled away from her towards the door, saying coldly, 'The door will be locked, and Stumpy will be on guard outside. I accept your word —for what it is worth.'

'Thank you. Oh, thank you!' Angelina cried, hardly able to conceal her triumph, and he flung a look over his shoulder which took all pleasure from the moment.

'When I return, we shall spend a little time together, and you can show your—appreciation—of my gentle-manly behaviour.' And then he was gone, and the sound of the key being turned in the lock brought Charity's head up once again. Angelina stood with a finger against her lips. She motioned the woman across to the far side of the room, and they sank together on to the bed.

'What are you looking so pleased about?' Charity hissed. 'You have given him your word. Foolish child!'

'Which I have no intention of keeping. I would have

promised anything to get him to leave me here. Anything, do you hear? We have a chance now. All we have to do is to entice that old man in here, and once we are rid of him, we shall be free to leave the ship. We shall be aboard the *White Swan* and heading towards the open sea before Raven returns. Captain Forrester knows these waters, Charity. If necessary, we shall put into some deserted cove and wait it out.'

CHAPTER
FIVE

AFTER DINNER, Angelina and Charity idled away the afternoon hours somehow. No one came near them again until Stumpy brought them an evening meal, although both women had heard frequent footsteps pacing the corridor, often halting outside the cabin and then moving off again. How many men had Raven left on board? Angelina wondered. One, perhaps two men on watch, and Stumpy. She prayed that there were not more . . . three would be difficult enough. She refused to consider the idea that her scheme would not succeed. It had to. Her liberty—nay, more than that—depended on it.

She picked at her food, growing restless and irritable. As soon as dusk descended over the water, shrouding the ship in lengthening grey shadows, she changed into her boy's clothes and pushed her hair beneath a woollen cap. Tortuga waterfront was no place for a lady to be seen, even though she intended spending no more than a few minutes on it. That was how long she estimated it would take them to steal down the gangplank and on board the *White Swan*. While Charity engaged the watch, she would free her crew and then the ship would be hers again. The tide was turning, a strong breeze beginning to whip the tops of the waves. They would have no trouble slipping away unseen from the harbour. At least that was what she told herself—and Charity —over and over again. To contemplate failure was to give herself into Raven's tender care as she had promised.

Never, never, never! she vowed, as Charity lighted a roof lantern. On deck, the watch called eight bells. It was time. Her heart in her mouth, she began to rap loudly on the door to attract attention. When Stumpy came to unlock it, she would be hiding against the bulkhead, waiting to knock him unconscious with a heavy brass candlestick. There came the sound of footsteps, and she caught her breath, her eyes widening as she stared across to where Charity stood by the window, a hand pressed against her racing heart. What if it was not Stumpy, but another seaman, less gullible and unsuspecting?

The door swung open, and a man moved over the threshold into the light. It *was* Stumpy, and his attention immediately directed towards Charity gave Angelina all the time she needed. With all her might she brought the object she held down across the back of his head, and with a groan, he dropped to the floor in front of her. She stood stunned, horrified at the enormity of what she had done, only rousing herself when Charity flung down beside the man with a stifled cry. The fingers she laid against the balding head came away streaked with blood.

'Oh, what have we done?' the woman whispered, raising a distressed countenance to the girl, who quickly shut the door and began searching through the unconscious man's pockets. She brought to light a pistol, which she tucked into her belt, and a knife which was instantly thrown to the far side of the room with a shudder of distaste.

'It was necessary, Charity. Don't waste your sympathy on the man,' she said in surprise. Although he had been most courteous and helpful to them both, she found that to regard him in the same light as Raven and the rest of the pirates was the only way to justify the trickle of blood running down the back of his neck. It was too late to have regrets. 'It is done, and we are almost free. Quickly, follow me, and remember to lock the door after you.'

'I think I am going to faint,' Charity murmured weakly, as she continued to stare at the blood staining her fingers. It was obvious to Angelina that she was becoming increasing fond of this little man, which both surprised and worried her!

'For all his meek words, he would have obeyed his captain's orders, whatever they were,' the girl said firmly, 'and whatever hardship they caused us, he would not have cared. He was told to be nice to us—to allay our suspicions! To make us meek and mild so that we gave no trouble. No! He is like all the rest. Come along quickly.'

'I—I'm not sure I can go on with this,' Charity whispered, her cheeks ashen. She looked very nervous and Angelina sought to reassure her, putting her own fear behind her in doing so.

'Nonsense.' Taking out Charity's handkerchief, she wiped the red fingers clean, and then, with a grimace she was unable to hide, dropped the smeared linen on to Stumpy's unconscious form. Gently but firmly she then lifted the woman to her feet and planted a kiss on one white cheek. How cold her skin was, and her eyes had that strange, glazed look which always preceded confusion of the past and present. Dear God, she prayed, not now! Let her remain in control of her faculties until we are safe on board the *White Swan*. If ever she needed the comfort, the strength of a man, it was now.

She longed for her father's wise counsel, his quiet confidence which had instilled so much courage into her—but alas, she had no one to depend on but herself. She *was* capable! They would succeed!

Opening the cabin door, she drew Charity out into the passage. The woman was reluctant to follow, her gaze still intent on the man on the floor. Then, with a shudder which convulsed her whole body, she allowed herself to be drawn away. It was Angelina who locked the door after them and tossed the key into a dark recess.

Like silent shadows, always present, yet without voice, they stole to the companion. No sound from above. Mounting the stairs, Angelina helped Charity out behind her and pressed her back into the dimness while she accustomed herself to the half-light which now prevailed. Everywhere was deserted, apart from a sailor on the foredeck. The night watch! He was leaning over the rail, staring towards the shore, no doubt envying those making merry with women and wine in the many taverns which lined the harbour. The whole place was a den of iniquity, Angelina thought, horrified, never for one moment comparing it with the licentious life of the court she had left behind in England. This was, of course, far different!

She was glad of the diversion, for the noise and laughter being carried to the ship would help to cover their furtive movements, as would the creaking and groaning coming from her depths as she rocked at anchor.

Angelina loved to listen to a ship 'talking' in the night. On her first trip it had terrified her, for she had thought they were all imminently destined for a watery grave. How far away that first day seemed now, when as a twelve-year-old child she had stowed away to be with the father she adored, to try to be the son he had always wished for. To spend months at sea, marvelling at the new world opening up before her, groaning at the hard work with which she had been presented as a punishment for the worry she was causing to her mother at home with her untimely absence. A strong wind billowed through the rigging, wood creaked, from below came sounds to make old sailors turn in their graves, but she revelled in it all. This was her world . . .

Voices from in front of her sent the nostalgic moment fleeing from her mind. Another sailor had joined the watch. Two, now!

'We must make a move before the old man is missed,' she whispered, her lips close against Charity's ear. 'Stay low as you follow me, and if we are seen, run as though the devil were after you—for indeed he will be after me. Here'—she reached up and grabbed two belaying-pins from the rack beside her and pushed one in her companion's unresisting hands—'grip it tightly. If anyone—anyone at all—challenges us before we reach the *White Swan*, hit him and hit him hard.'

She doubted if Charity would ever do so, but *she* would—and with a vengeance! Stealthily she edged towards the gangplank. Neither man on the foredeck looked in their direction. They were talking and laughing, totally absorbed in what was going on ashore. Angelina could hardly believe it when they reached dry land unchallenged, and had to suppress a whoop of joy at her achievement. The shadowy outline of the *White Swan* was off to their left—with a bright patch of moonlight to cross before they reached it.

She froze once again as she heard voices, and almost fell on top of Charity in an effort to hide her as four laughing, very drunk and swaying pirates staggered towards them, changed their minds, and turned to disappear into an alley. Pray heaven to another tavern which would keep them occupied, Angelina thought, as she caught Charity's hand and eased her towards her ship. A hundred yards only, but it could have been a hundred miles. Alone, dressed as she was, she might have succeeded in bluffing the lounging men, the drunks and seamen who frequented the harbour at this time of night. Cut-throats and purse-snatchers, most of them, she suspected, out to make a few more coins for their pockets even if it meant robbing their fellow pirates. There was no honour among thieves! But with a dazed, stumbling old woman she had no chance. But of course she had! A wild idea surged through her brain. She bent to whisper to Charity—heard the startled, indeed horrified, response and ignored it. Giving her no chance to think about it, she pulled the woman to her feet.

Two figures stumbled from the shadows: one was a mere lad to all appearances, and not too well, judging from the way he held tightly to the arm of his companion —a woman of some considerable years, although not bad of figure in the moonlight. Her face was, well—it had once been quite pretty, or was so thought by those they passed, who watched them with amused eyes and followed their somewhat erratic wanderings across the quay with amused, sometimes bawdy, comments.

'We are almost there,' Angelina whispered, hugging Charity close to her. Let them think what they liked, the fools! A few more yards, and they would be at the gangplank of the *White Swan*. While Charity went on board and engaged the watch with whatever means she found necessary—she herself had suggested a swoon —Angelina intended to find the imprisoned crew and free them. It was madness, but it was all she had! And, so far, it had worked.

Dark shapes loomed up in their path. Before she could open her mouth, or grab the pistol, a rough hand went over her mouth and she was held in a vice-like grip. Charity was treated in the same manner. Someone made a joke about showing the young lad and his aged companion where they could enjoy themselves for the night, and they were propelled forcibly into a darkened alley, helpless against the strong arms that held them.

'The capitán was right—your word means nothing, lovely English lady,' Raúl whispered in her ear, snatching the belaying-pin from her belt. Angelina went suddenly faint with horror. It had all been for nothing? *He* had allowed her to go to all this effort—to experience this fear, the nausea which rose in her stomach when she thought of what could happen to her at the hands of those Tortuga pirates—all for nothing! He had expected her to escape? She sagged in Raúl's arms, for it was he who held her, her senses reeling for many minutes. When she recovered, she found herself being propelled at a fast rate through endless streets. Her hands were bound behind her and she was enveloped in a heavy cloak, the cowl drawn over her features so that they were not readily visible to passers-by.

Her legs turned to water with the realisation that he was taking her to Raven for punishment. She had lied —and he had known it from the start. He had wanted her to escape, to watch her futile efforts. The monster! The inhuman coward, to enjoy seeing her suffer so! Was this the way he intended to break her spirit? She had been so sure of herself—so confident that her plan would work—but he had played her like a helpless fish caught on a spiked line, hauling her in when the fancy took him. He was—she had no word for the loathing and disgust which swept over her—he was the spawn of the devil, cursed by all God-fearing men! There was not one spark of humanity in him. And she was his to do with as he pleased!

She stumbled and fell, and was hauled to her feet again with a roughness that made her blood boil despite the terrible fear which made her limbs feel weak and useless. She had no weapon against such a man. Here, in this place—indeed, wherever he was—he was all powerful. She was a chattel!

Some way behind she heard Charity cry out, and tried to stop, but Raúl urged her on without mercy. One day he, too, would pay for the grief he was causing them both, she vowed. He would stand alongside his accursed captain and accept the penalty for his crimes.

'In here.' Raúl opened a door and pushed her through. She cringed at the entrance of a place such as she had never seen before. The gags were removed from the mouths of both women. Smoke choked her, and the odour of unwashed bodies, stale ale and so many aromas she was unaccustomed to accepting. 'You look a little green, my lady.' A hand in her back propelled her forward. 'I suggest you do exactly as I say unless you want us to fight over you. While the capitán may be quite willing to do that to keep you, I am sure you would not want it. He may lose, you see and then you could belong to "Big Red" over there.' He pointed to a heavily bearded giant lounging in a chair, a dark-skinned woman splayed across his lap and showing more than a fair share of shapely leg as he caressed her thighs. 'Or Capitán Death. Now *he* is a man of taste. He prefers red-headed virgins . . .' Angelina found herself face to face with a skeleton of a man with black piercing eyes and a sallow skin. The cruel mouth deepened into a sardonic smile as Raúl ushered her past. 'You look like a cabin-lad at this moment, my lady. For your own sake and that of the capitán in whose hands your worthless life rests, I suggest you do exactly as you are told. Utter no word—not one, do you hear?'

Mutely Angelina nodded as she was thrust down on to a hard seat, and across the oak table, littered with bottles and pewter tankards, found herself face to face with —Raven.

'You found her, then?' he said casually. The beast! Did he have no compassion for the tight ropes which were chafing her wrists? He could see that she was tied! His gaze raked coldly over her before he drained his tankard.

'Where you said she might be, Capitán. She gave us no trouble.' He grinned as Charity was dumped unceremoniously beside them like a sack of grain.

'Give her some Madeira, I believe it does her good,' Raven murmured, as the woman sagged half-fainting across the table.

'No,' Angelina cried. 'You will . . . Oh, you swine, you know what it will do to her!'

'Hold your tongue, wench, unless you want to find yourself up for auction to the highest bidder. If I am going to have this much trouble with you, I am of a mind to sell you and recoup what I have already paid out to get you. I am beginning to think you are not worth it.' Raven's cold tones silenced her protests. Behind the black mask, his eyes bored into her pale face. 'You are a liar and a cheat. I can find a more honest woman from among the whores here tonight.'

'Those you would have to pay! To abduct one of them would be rather a waste of time . . . They have nothing to lose.' Angelina spat the words at him venomously. How dare he think of degrading her even more!

'Have you? As the prospective bride of Edgar Sarandon, you will have lost your innocence a long time ago.'

She gasped as though he had struck her, and as he watched the last of the colour ebb from her cheeks, Raven knew that she still retained the highest prize of all to give to a man. She had belonged to no man—would belong to no man—until she belonged to him, body and soul.

So he had to get her safely back to his ship before anyone discovered what lay beneath those loose, uninteresting clothes. If she uttered one wrong word, he would have the devil of a fight on his hands. That in itself he did not mind, but he did not want to endanger her life. If only she had trusted him, and come with him willingly, his business could have been completed without any fuss—without arousing suspicion—and he would have wined and dined her as if she were a queen among men, in safe, suitable surroundings.

Instead she had lied to him, deliberately set out to trick him, and in doing so aroused him to great anger. He did not blame her for trying to escape. She was a girl of great spirit and he had always expected her to fight him—for a little while, at least. It was her cool, devious deception that had plunged him into a black mood. Even men he had known for many years turned away from the table where he sat drinking when they saw the scowl on his face.

Suspicion was rife in Tortuga, on every street corner, in every tavern and in the mind of every man who lived outside the law, for their very lives were forfeit if their sanctuary was ever invaded. It was not only the most notorious haven in the Caribbean, but the safest, and its inhabitants intended it to remain thus.

The captain of each ship in port was responsible for dealing out justice to any wrong-doer among his crew. If, for some reason, he found himself unable to pronounce a sentence, the accused was passed on to the Captains of the Coast, the select twelve whose word was final. The island had its own heartless brand of justice and there was no appeal against their decision, which was why most men preferred the rough justice of a man they sailed under to that cruel inhumanity dealt out by the twelve.

'Capitán, I think in a moment we could have company,' Raúl said in a low tone.

'Enrico?' Raven enquired, and received a nod of affirmation.

'By the door, talking with two of this men. He has been looking this way since he came in. I knew we were not the only ones watching for the girl. Somehow he knew she was aboard. If he laid hands on her, he could ask a fine ransom for her, eh?' Angelina flushed uncomfortably as he looked at her with a wicked grin. His tone told her that she held no interest for him, apart from the money he could get for delivering her safely back to Edgar or for selling her in some slave market.

'Who from—Sarandon? The man who pays him to attack her ships and send them to the bottom of the sea?' Raven exclaimed, and she gasped at the insinuation. 'He'd see her dead before he raised a finger to help her.'

'That's a lie! A wicked, monstrous lie!' Angelina said fiercely. 'Edgar loves me. He would do anything and pay any amount to get me back.'

'My dear girl, are you a complete simpleton where that man is concerned? He hasn't a decent emotion in his whole body. He has only one love—money—and he would not part with a single coin to get you back. What he has had from you he can get from others.' He was angry, and wanted to hurt her. As she sagged back against the high-backed oak settle, he saw he had succeeded. 'Cut her free, Raúl—and you, sit still and remain quiet,' he added, as she straightened immediately. Folding his arms upon the table between them, he leaned towards her, his eyes burning into her pale face. 'Tell me, who is managing your affairs while you are sailing the high seas, proving your worth in a man's world?'

'Why, Edgar, of course! Who better than the man I am to marry?' she flung back hotly, hating him for speaking to her so in front of Raúl and the grinning sailor who had helped to capture her.

'Was to have married,' Raven corrected. 'Have I not already explained that you will never set eyes on him again? By now, you will be lucky to have a single farthing left in the bank, and most likely he will have defaulted with all your creditors. You would return to empty coffers, my angel, and only the sale of your ships, so generously handed over upon your wedding day, would clear his debts. Edgar Sarandon never could keep his hands off others people's property—whatever it was . . .' He broke off, a fierce frown furrowing his black brows, and for a moment, as she gazed at him, Angelina wondered if she were not looking at the devil himself, so satanic was his expression, so murderous the gleam in those cold eyes.

Of course Edgar had his faults—no man was perfect —but to suggest that he would rob her, or leave her to be abused and degraded by pirates, no, never! Raven's insulting suggestions left her speechless. As soon as the

White Swan became overdue in port, he would send another ship to look for her, might even come himself.

'Oh, if only I had my pistol,' she fumed, finding her voice at last.

'If you shoot me, you would be in a pretty pickle. If my *amigo* Raúl did not kill you, you would find yourself at the mercy of every cut-throat in this room. As you will, if you utter one word to give away your identity.' Angelina knew he was right. She was as helpless here, even though she was on dry land again, as she would have been on his ship miles out to sea. She wanted to jump to her feet and beg someone to help her, but as she looked at the hard, weathered faces and heard the coarse laughter echoing about her and watched how the women in the tavern displayed themselves to attract attention, she knew that to do so would be to place her life in great danger.

'I am glad to see you have at least one sensible thought in your head,' Raven murmured, as her eyes flickered back to his face. He had been watching her, she realised. It was almost as though he could read her mind. It was uncanny—frightening! 'I think we all need refreshments to relax us.'

He caught the eye of a buxom serving-girl, and minutes later four enormous tankards of red wine were brought to the table. He tossed a coin into the waiting hand with a grin that told Angelina he was no stranger here—or to the woman who gave him an inviting look before she walked away, her full hips swinging provocatively. Her hair was dyed, she thought, and her face heavily rouged. Was that the kind of woman he associated with? Aware of his eyes on her again, she quickly looked away, not wanting him to guess her thoughts this time—it would be too humiliating if he thought she *cared* whom he slept with. Did she? Was his dangerous charm reaching out to her even in this place, to remind her how it was when he held her in his arms, how she had enjoyed his masterful kisses?

'Drink up, angel! You are supposed to be a boy, remember? Act like one,' Raven ordered, pushing a full tankard towards her.

He expected her to drink this foul-smelling rough wine? She could hardly lift the tankard, let alone consume the contents, but beneath his steely gaze she managed a few mouthfuls before thrusting it away from her, barely able to conceal a grimace of disgust.

'Rather a young addition to your crew, isn't he, Captain? Or have you taken a fancy to pretty boys these days?' a voice drawled close beside them, and Angelina's head jerked up in horror.

The man who stood behind Raven was squat like an oversize pudding—and grotesque! His brightly-coloured shirt and tight-fitting trousers accentuated the rolls of fat about his waist, the podgy wrists and thick, hairy fingers. A wide-brimmed hat was set on the back of his head, on top of a long curled wig. The kind one of King Charles's courtiers would wear, she thought, hardly able to believe her eyes—but this creature was no courtier! Long seaboots fitted so snugly about his thick thighs that she wondered how he ever managed to extricate himself from them.

Without turning in his seat, Raven said in a cool tone, 'You are interrupting a private conversation, Gonzalves. Go back to your sty before someone stuffs an apple in your mouth and serves you up for dinner.'

The answer brought great guffaws of laughter from near by tables—and two bright red spots of angry colour to the cheeks of Enrico Gonzalves. So this was the man who had tried to attack the *White Swan*; whom Raven accused of pillaging her cargoes and killing her men! She took an instant dislike to him. His eyes were small brown darting beads, never still. She did not like the way they looked at her, and was glad of the heavy cloak which covered her body.

'A very pretty boy . . . I could use a lad like him. I need a new cabin-boy.' Angelina was aware of Raúl tensing beside her as Enrico's hand rested lightly on the hilt of his sword. Was it his intention to provoke a fight with Raven? It was obvious that there was no love lost between them. 'Give him to me . . . as consolation, shall we say, for thwarting my attack on that Blackthorne ship the other day. You owe it to me. She was mine.'

'No—on both counts.' Slowly Raven turned to look up at the man behind him. He appeared in no way concerned by the rudeness thrown at him, but Angelina sensed that he, too, was tensed ready for a fight. To spring at the fat little man with the agility, and the deadly prowess of a jungle cat. 'I would no more hand the lad over to you than I would have left him with the Spaniards from whom I took him and who had just killed his parents. The shock has struck him dumb, so you will not hear a word from his lips.' How easily he lied . . . and saved her from betraying that she was no boy. Charity was sitting bolt upright in her seat, her face rigid with fear. Angelina prayed that she would not utter a sound. Poor Charity, she was scarcely over one nightmare before she was launched into another! She could find it in her heart to hate Raven for that reason alone. 'As for the *White Swan*, she is one Blackthorne ship you will not plunder. You will have to send word to your master that you failed this time. Send him the compliments of the

Raven. If he wants her back, he can come and get her himself.'

And with that, he turned his back on the man and proceeded to drain his tankard, but Angelina saw that his eyes were watching Raúl—he would know of any movement from behind.

'Damn your eyes, Raven! You've crossed me for the last time. You know full well what was aboard that ship,' the man growled, turning nearly purple now as men near by grinned and nudged each other, and once again he saw his prestige sinking among them.

'A worthwhile cargo, I admit,' Raven replied, his eyes momentarily switching to Angelina's anxious face as he spoke. 'But nothing of great value.'

The insufferable beast! She wanted to hit him, but silently cursed him instead in the most unladylike manner, aware of the laughter flickering in those grey depths as they acknowledged her chagrin.

'No value, eh?' Captain Gonzalves swung round on the listening crowd. 'Hear me, men. No value? He lies in his teeth. There will be a fat reward—and I mean real money—for anyone who brings me the captain of the *White Swan*.'

'Are you going in for older men, Capitán?' Raúl chuckled. 'You always did have appalling taste—in everything.' As his gaze rested on the striped shirt and outrageously tight breeches, everyone in the room exploded into laughter.

'You young snake! I should have killed you when I had the chance!' His sword came sliding out of its scabbard, but with only half the blade free, he was stopped. The fingers which closed around his wrist made him yelp in pain. A burly sailor—his bodyguard, Angelina suspected, for he had been standing very close by throughout the conversation—started forward menacingly, only to be struck down by a man at his side. Somehow Raúl was out from behind the table, a wicked knife gleaming in one hand as he faced the few men who had risen, hoping for a fight. At the smile lingering on his lips, the sensible ones gracefully retired into the background.

'Not then—and not now,' Raven snapped, and Enrico screamed in pain as the grip on him tightened.

Raven's hand fell to the knife at his belt and watched Enrico's face grow white with fear. The confounded man! He deserved to die for what he had had in mind. Angelina in his power! Raven was incensed at the thought. What, then? Ransom? He doubted it. Edgar's orders would have been explicit. Dispose of the unwanted baggage when she had served her purpose, and make it look as if the abduction and subsequent murder had been committed by another—probably himself!

A dainty morsel she would have been for Enrico's scurvy crew of cut-throats, and for anyone else who took a fancy to her. It made his blood boil to think what she would have endured before the end came to release her from pain and fear. The man did not deserve to live.

His fingers tightened on the hilt of the knife. It was half-way out of the leather sheath, when Gonzalves screamed,

'Damn it, man, you are breaking my wrist!'

'I would prefer it to be your head,' a loud voice declared. 'Will you never learn, Captain? I'm of a mind to let Raven take you apart. It is a spectacle I should enjoy immensely.'

The figure who strode towards them was tall and powerful, dressed in elegant clothes of rich velvet, a plumed hat shadowing a sun-bronzed face that was working furiously. Halting before the two men, he surveyed them, his hands on his hips . . . and everyone in the room, including Angelina, held their breath as they waited for him to speak again. It was a though his appearance has cast a spell over the whole throng. No one moved—or spoke. All eyes were fastened expectantly on the new arrival.

'Let him go, Raven. Much as I would enjoy the sight of him with his head on a pike, you must delay the happy event a while longer. I'm only in port one night, and I don't intend to waste a moment of it. We have some bottles to drain and wenches to accommodate.'

With a contemptuous gesture, Raven flung Enrico backwards so violently that he could not keep his balance; he grabbed for a table and missed, and there was a great rending sound as he sprawled to the floor. It was a very embarrassed, red-faced man uttering a string of unintelligible oaths who hastened from the room, followed by cat-calls and derisive obscenities.

'Raven, my boy, he will not forget this one either. One day you will have to slit his throat and put him out of his misery.'

'How are you, Henry? It's good to see your ugly Welsh face again!'

Henry Morgan laughed as he slapped the younger man heartily on the back. They embraced like long-lost brothers while Angelina looked on in open-mouthed astonishment. This was the bloodthirsty pirate who had sacked Porto Bello? Attacked Maracaibo with such savagery? He had a kind face, and the bearing of a gentleman. Yet so, too, had Raven . . . The thought made her inwardly shiver.

'I've a keg of good rum in the back room.' Luckily

Henry Morgan's interest in her was diverted by a smiling, dark-haired girl who brought him a bombard of the house speciality, which smelled even worse than the wine. 'And wenches—the best in Tortuga.' He slipped a coin into the cleavage of her low-cut blouse, kissed her soundly and sent her on her way with a slap across her pert bottom. 'What's this I hear about you bringing in an English ship? Have you grown tired of chasing Spaniards?'

'Our paths just happened to cross, and she was such an attractive prize that I couldn't resist her,' Raven replied casually.

His eyes flickered to where Angelina sat. Anger still lingered in the grey smouldering depths. For her, or Enrico, she wondered? He had wanted to fight the man, she thought, but he could not, for fear her identity would inadvertently be revealed. However much she loathed her present position as his prisoner, she was forced to admit that only he stood between her and the pack of hungry wolves who would descend on her if they discovered she was a woman—and a beautiful one at that!

'I'll join you in a little while, after I've settled our young friend here upstairs.' His arm was beneath her elbow, drawing her to her feet. She rose obediently. She could not quit the presence of these pirates soon enough.

'Be quick about it then, laddie. I want to hear about this great prize you have acquired.' His amused gaze rested once again on Angelina's face. Did he suspect? She held her breath, and felt Raven's fingers tighten painfully over her arm as the words struck a sour note in his mind also.

'Captain, I wish to be taken back on board your ship,' Charity said in a low, but very determined tone as Henry Morgan turned away. 'I am concerned for—for the old man. We should not have hit him so hard,' she added, lifting apologetic eyes to Angelina's startled face.

'Stumpy!' The fingers holding her were now biting so agonisingly into her skin that Angelina had to bite her lip to prevent herself from crying out. Raven's eyes blazed behind the mask as they searched her guilty face. 'You have much to answer for—both of you!'

'It was none of Charity's doing,' she murmured, determined that he should not intimidate her—and exceedingly conscious of the many eyes which were upon them, including those of Henry Morgan, who had paused on the far side of the room to look back to where they stood. 'I hit him, and I would do it again. Anything to escape from you.'

'That you will never do. Raúl, take her back as she wishes. See that she cares for Stumpy until we return. Send word to me here as to his condition.'

'Ay, Capitán.'

'You, Benson, come with me,' Raven ordered the other seaman, and strode towards the flight of stairs which led up to another floor with him not a step behind them. Angelina was growing ever more afraid of what was to happen to her once they were alone as she stumbled after him.

She was thrust into a small room which sported only a large bed, a table and a wash-stand, where a solitary candle cast flickering shadows over the bare walls. A large window opened out on to a wrought-iron balcony. As she started towards it, the door slammed shut behind her. Raven's cold tones snapped, 'It's a long drop, and I would prefer you in one piece to receive a suitable punishment for this night's piece of mischief.'

She swung round and found him watching her growing

agitation with steely eyes. The candlelight cast a long shadow on the wall beside him, an enormous, menacing black shape which moved slowly towards her. What did he intend to do with her? Take her here and now?

The bed was behind her, so she could go no further. She flung out a trembling hand to stave him off as he reached for her, but it was brushed roughly aside. He tore off the woollen cap that confined her hair, and as it tumbled free about her shoulders, his fingers fastened in it and she was pulled against his chest. Even in the dimness of the drab room, she could see the fury glittering in his eyes.

'You are a liar—and a cheat! You never intended to keep your word, did you?'

When she was slow in answering, he tugged back her head and she moaned with the pain.

'No! No! Why should I keep my word to you—a pirate! What do you know of honesty—truth—integrity?' she cried tremulously.

'More than you, it seems. My given word has never been broken. That in itself was bad enough, but what you did to that old man . . . I am uncommonly fond of him, I would have you know.'

'What will you do to me, Captain?' She spat the word at him with the last of her swiftly fading defiance. 'Whip me? Sell me to your friends? Yes, why not? Sell me, I want you to. Anything to be free of you!'

'No man shall have you but me,' Raven told her, his voice dropping to a silken caress that terrified her more than his anger. He slid an arm round her back, pressing her against the leather of his doublet. She turned her face away as she felt his warm breath against her cheek, and heard him chuckle.

'Yes, I think I have a fitting punishment for you, my

angel. As you have no regard for promises, I see no reason for me to keep mine.'

'What—What do you mean?' she whispered, limp in his grasp. His very nearness was having that same devastating effect on her, wiping from her mind all thought of what he was and had done—all she was aware of were his lips against her cheek. She shuddered, but not altogether from fear. The gold buckle which fastened the sash across his chest dug deeper into her breast as he tightened his hold on her and brought her face closer to his. 'I shall scream, if—if . . .'

'No, you will not cry out, for you well know what manner of man will come to your aid, and the reward he will expect—and demand—for his services,' Raven mocked, brushing her lips lightly with his own. How his eyes burned with triumph when she did not try to turn away from him again, she saw. She could not. 'What do you fear most in your life, I wonder? Abduction, force, to be sold in a Maracaibo slave market? Tempting as that idea is to me at this moment after your deception, I shall not let you go. You see, I know why you tremble so when I look at you—when I hold you.' He was loosening the fastenings of her cloak as he spoke, pushing it away from her shoulders until it slid to the floor. Bold fingers traced the curve of her breast beneath the linen shirt. His touch burned her as though it was against her naked flesh. 'It is not even me you fear, but yourself. You are beginning to like my kisses, angel.'

'No! You are wrong . . . I hate you!'

'Love? Hate? Neither emotion has anything to do with the way you feel when I touch you. I have roused the woman in you, and you like it.'

It was true, and she hated him more for knowing it, because it was the one weapon he could use against her for which she had no defence.

'As you have seen fit to break your word to me, then there is no reason why I should honour my pledge not to touch you until after we had left here. Think on it while I am downstairs with Morgan, and be ready for me when I return. I shall stand no false show of modesty.'

Angelina was released so unexpectedly that she fell back on the bed and lay there dazed, disbelieving that he was leaving her without exacting his due. From the doorway, his voice came softly to her, sealing her fate.

'There will be a man outside until I return—should you be stupid enough to try and leave.'

To guard her, deprive her of her freedom, as he did! With a cry of despair she turned her face into the pillow, overcome with a fit of weeping which, when it eventually subsided, left her weak and lightheaded—and in no doubt as to the seriousness of Raven's intentions. He would come to her and take her even if she was unwilling . . . but the moment he touched her, she knew that her treacherous body would be aroused. She was no woman of easy virtue, so how had it come about that he could tempt her thus?

She was lost and helpless against him and the fires he kindled within her. He had shown her the passionate spirit that had dwelled dormant deep inside her until he had come with his mocking devil's eyes, his confident demands—and now she had no control over it. She would not surrender herself to him, even though it was what she wanted. She could never hold her head erect again if she did—yet had she not promised to belong to him in return for the safety of the *White Swan* and her crew? And he had kept his word, for Stumpy had confirmed that they were all in good health and being well treated. But for how long? How long before he tired of her?

She turned over and lay on her back, staring at the shadows the candlelight cast round the room, oblivious to the raucous laughter drifting up from below. Quite often heavy footsteps went past the door, but no one attempted to enter. With one of Raven's men outside, it was more than a life was worth, she thought.

Perhaps he would not come . . . Perhaps he had found a woman. If he did . . . Her eyelids dropped wearily, and sleep came unbidden to her exhausted mind, without the agonising question being answered.

CHAPTER
SIX

ANGELINA AWOKE with the realisation that she was no longer alone. Her first assumption was that Raven had returned, and she sat up, drawing herself back against the wall. But the guttural tones that cursed the chair into which the man blundered as he made his way across the darkened room struck terror into her heart. The candle had blown out in a strong breeze from the open window, and she had not bothered to drag herself from the bed to rekindle it. It was not Raven come to claim her—then who! And how had he got past the guard left outside the door? Instinct told her that the man would not have left his post. He was either unconscious or dead—and she was at the mercy of whoever was near by.

Perhaps she could reach the door before he knew she was there . . . She had barely eased herself to the end of the bed and was preparing to fling herself at the door —or at least in the direction she thought it might be for she could make nothing out in the inky blackness, when the candle flared to life. She gave a cry of terror as, turned in her direction, she saw the heavily bearded face of the giant—Enrico's bodyguard who had attempted to stab Raven from behind!

In panic she scrambled from the bed, but one booted foot became entangled in the bedclothes and she pitched heavily to the floor. Before she could move again, the man was upon her, a hairy hand clapped across her mouth, choking off a scream meant to bring help . . . anyone at all, even Raven!

'What have we here then? No pretty cabin-boy, but a wench—and a comely one at that!' She was held in a bear-like grip while he surveyed her. 'Capt'n Enrico were right after all—the *White Swan* did have a captain in petticoats aboard.'

Angelina fought like a wild animal in his grasp, more afraid than she had ever been in her life before. From the way he was looking at her, she knew he would have no respect for her womanhood. As lithe as a cat, she twisted in his grasp and kicked backwards with the heel of her boot. The man swore as it connected with his shin, and then swore again as she managed to free her lips from his hand long enough to sink her teeth into the back of it.

'You bitch!' He dealt her a savage blow across the face which sent her reeling back on the bed, where she lay too stunned to resist further as he lugged her over on to her stomach, jerked her arms cruelly behind her back and securely tied her wrists together with a piece of coarse rope pulled from his breeches. An evil-smelling handkerchief was bound over her mouth, and she lay with head swimming and cheek throbbing madly, desperately fighting down the urge to vomit.

The man rolled her over on to her back again, and chuckled as he saw the bruise already beginning to appear on one cheek. A calloused hand reached out to explore her breasts, and he gave a broad smile as he discovered the softness which was concealed by the linen shirt.

'Ay, a comely wench. Not the boy the capt'n was expecting, and that will be a disappointment to him —but you'll do for me. I'll find him another handsome lad to warm his bed. You'll do well for me, wench. I shall get hours of pleasure out of you—but not yet,' he added, as Angelina's eyes dilated with fear. 'First there is Raven to deal with—and then . . .'

She closed her eyes with a shudder of disgust. From one captor into the arms of another, far more terrible than Raven, although until this moment she had not thought she could fear another man as she did him, knowing what he wanted from her. This one would show her no mercy whatsoever. Where was Raven? How long had she been asleep that he had not yet returned to claim her? What was detaining him? A bottle of rum or a willing woman?

The man glanced round towards the door, and then turned to look at her with narrowed eyes. As she wondered what he had in store for her now, he lifted her back against the wall so that she was facing it and would be directly in the line of vision of whoever entered. Hooking his fingers in the front of her shirt, he ripped it open, exposing her to his lecherous gaze, his eyes gleaming as a low moan came from behind the gag.

'The first—and only—thing Raven will ever see will be you. At least he'll die happy.'

Desperate tears sprang to her eyes as he rose from her side and took up a position to one side of the door. He would be behind it when it was opened—and Raven's reaction to the sight of her lying bound and gagged, half-naked, would give him the advantage he needed. She knew now that Gonzalves had sent him to kill Raven . . . to kill him and abduct her, not knowing that she was a woman. In a short while she might well belong to this monster who lounged against the wall, his gaze constantly raking over her loveliness.

She could do nothing . . . make no sound. She had no way of warning Raven what awaited him. But she had to—she could not lie here and watch him die before her eyes, surrender herself to the advances of her new captor, without a fight. Yet there was little left in her . . . she was tired and frightened. She had gone from one nightmare to another so quickly that her mind had not yet accepted the change. And then she shifted her position as cramp invaded her right leg, and the rope binding her cut painfully into her wrists to jolt her back to the reality of her situation. The pain brought back memory—the giant's words, 'The *White Swan* did have a captain in petticoats aboard.' They meant only one thing—Raven had noticed! Enrico Gonzalves had attacked Blackthorne ships in the past and had been intending to abduct her, too!

Whatever the hour, there was still laughter and merry-making going on downstairs. Who would hear the sound of a body falling to the floor? Who would care in this vice-den? She turned her head to lay her aching cheek against the cold wall and saw, then, the nail protruding at an angle from the side of the bedpost. The curtain had been torn away from it at some point and never been repaired.

Footsteps outside . . . going past. Not Raven. Wait, they were returning . . . The man left his position long enough to snuff out the candle, plunging the room once more into total blackness. Angelina threw herself forward so quickly that her head connected with the oak post, almost stunning her again. She felt the nail repeatedly scratch her cheek as she feverishly worked to hook the cloth about her mouth over it. With each movement of her head as she tugged, jerked it to and fro in a growing panic, the pain increased, yet she was hardly aware of it. Any minute she expected the man to turn and see her, and thwart her brave efforts.

The door began to open. Her lips were free! The

scream which was torn from them was so piercing that it completely shattered the giant's intense concentration. He wheeled about, uncertain whether to silence her or to launch himself at his now-warned prey the moment the door was flung open.

What happened next was a blur before Angelina's tear-streaked vision. Raven's tall shape momentarily filled the open doorway—for an instant he seemed to stand transfixed by the sight of the dishevelled, sobbing girl on the bed. She screamed at him again, thinking he was unaware of the figure menacing him.

'Behind the door! He means to kill you!'

But before the words were out of her mouth, the heavy door was slammed savagely against the gigantic frame behind it.

The man roared in pain as blood spurted from his nose as he came away from the wall to find himself facing Raven—armed with a knife and ready for him—and there was death in the grey eyes glittering behind the silken mask. The realisation that he had dropped his own weapon halted him in mid-stride. With a contemptuous gesture Raven motioned to the knife on the floor.

'Pick it up. This is the second time you have tried to kill me, Sharlock. There will not be a third!'

'I'll give Capt'n Enrico your head on a platter,' came the furious retort, as a grimy hand was wiped across a blood-streaked chin. Without warning, he launched himself at his opponent. Raven easily sidestepped, and his blade sliced the man's left arm, bringing another grunt of pain to his lips.

'I am not a helpless woman, Sharlock. I am not bound. You should not have touched her. I am going to kill you for that.'

Angelina's breath caught in her throat at the softly

spoken words. To take the life of another human being because he had laid hands on her! Why should he care if she was bruised a little? His way of bringing her to heel was more subtle, that was all—both men still wanted the same thing from her! She did not want to watch the encounter, for Raven seemed determined to reduce the other man slowly to a bleeding wreck before he killed him, slicing through shirt and skin repeatedly in calculated attacks which drove him back against the wall. But she could not help herself . . . she had never encountered such a violent spectacle before. Surely Raven did not really mean to kill him? His movements were precise —and deadly—and without mercy! He did!

With wide eyes she watched the bloodied figure of Sharlock sink to his knees, clutching at his stomach, where his life-blood was spilling out over his torn shirt. Raven stepped back and watched him topple over on to the floor, where he lay still. It was several minutes before he wiped his blade clean, and turned towards the bed. He had saved her—yet, even so, Angelina shrank back as he bent to cut through the ropes that bound her before replacing the knife in his boot, and the fear mirrored in the green depths of her eyes made him exclaim quietly,

'It's over . . . You are safe now.'

He slipped down beside her, gently raising her into a sitting position. His fingers touched her bruised cheek, and traced the path of the scratches beside her mouth, his features growing visibly grimmer as he realised the discomfort she was in.

'I wish he was alive, so that I could kill him all over again for these,' he said, and she stared at him as if he had taken leave of his senses. How tender was the look in his eyes, how gentle his voice—as if he really cared for her. 'No one . . . No one shall ever again hurt you,

Angelina. I swear it! I should not have lingered so long with Morgan, but I was angry with you. I wanted to break this rebellion in you by making you think I was coming back to make love to you. The longer I made you wait, and dread my return, the more you might be willing to keep to our bargain. And, in doing so, I caused you to be subjected to this . . .'

She quivered as he leaned forward and laid his lips against first her throbbing cheek and then the marks at the corners of her mouth. 'Without your warning, I would have been a dead man for sure. Is that not what you want?'

'I would rather face a hundred like you than one—one of him,' Angelina blurted out, tears starting to her eyes again. She did not understand this show of concern which seemed so genuine—but she desperately needed it after all she had been through. Only when Raven drew back from her with a soft expletive did she realised what she had said.

'Perhaps we have come together after all . . . But I would not have wished it this way . . . You must believe that.'

She would have believed anything he said to her in that moment as his arms went round her, drawing her close against his chest. The dead man lying a few feet away from them was forgotten as Raven's lips caressed her hair, her cheek, found her mouth. For the first time ever she found comfort in the arms which held her, a mounting joy in the possessiveness of his kiss. She was no longer afraid of the fire which leapt through her body, and clutched at him, feeling the hardness of his strong shoulders beneath her hands. As her lips opened beneath his, answering him, her body moulded against him in total surrender. She knew that no other man would ever make her feel as he had the power to do.

From the moment he had abducted her, she had denied the attraction she knew that she sensed. She could do so no longer. She would keep her bargain with him, not because she feared him, but because she had at last come to realise what it was she had been refusing to accept. She had fallen in love with Raven!

The tears which came suddenly were an outlet for her reeling emotions . . . Raven cradled her against him, stroking her hair, not speaking until the floodtide had passed. Sharlock with his brutal ways had succeeded where he had failed with subtlety. He would never have used force to have her, despite his occasional intimation to her that he might—it was not his way.

They would sail away from Tortuga, and he would make her forget that tonight had ever happened. He would remember it, though, and recall how the softness of her against him, the sudden explosion of passion on her kiss, had told him that she was his. Totally his! There were other obstacles looming on the horizon which might threaten this new-found joy, but he would surmount them somehow, now that she belonged to him, and he put them out of his mind.

'Capitán . . .' Raúl stood in the open doorway, and behind him, curious faces peered over his shoulder to see into the room, at broken furniture, the dead man, the red-haired beauty half-naked on the bed. Raven had not given a thought to the noise of the fight and the attention he had possibly attracted, and he cared even less, but as Angelina came away from him with a gasp, aware of her gaping shirt and clutching it together, bright colour staining her wet cheeks, he put her to one side, his expression warning his second-in-command to take care with his words—and stood up. 'We thought

you might need a little help, Capitán . . . I can see you
do not. One of the men found Benson in an alley outside
a few minutes ago, with his throat cut. I suspected you
might have uninvited company.'

'Please make them go away,' Angelina whispered.
The gaping mouths now began to whisper at the sight of
her torn clothing, the long fiery tresses cascading over
her shoulders—hidden from view before beneath a cap.
Speculations as to what had happened to her—who she
was—and what she would be worth at a sale, she supposed, as one man thrust his head round the doorpost
and ogled her leeringly. The flat of Raúl's hand hand
sent him reeling back into the crowd. 'Please.'

'Ask Wilma to bring some clean water and cloths,'
Raven ordered his second-in-command. He pointed to
the nearest two men. 'You—drag Sharlock out of here.
Deliver him to Captain Gonzalves with the Raven's
compliments. Should he wish to pursue the matter further, I shall be here. Tell him I would welcome the
opportunity to deal with his treachery personally. If I
catch one glimpse of him before I leave in the morning, I
shall. And someone bring me a bottle so that I can wash
this bad taste from my mouth.'

With narrowed, burning eyes, he surveyed the men
before him. 'Look all you wish, my friends, but remember what happened to Sharlock before you get any ideas
about touching this woman. He died because he dared to
lay hands on Raven's woman! Don't forget that.'

When they were alone, he strode to the door and
slammed it shut. He saw that Angelina's gaze was fixed
on the pool of blood where Sharlock had lain. She was
trembling again, and there were fresh tears in her eyes.
Shutting the window, he brought the candle closer to the
bed, set it down, and began to remove her boots. This

done, he made her get into bed properly and pulled the covers over her, completely hiding her ruined shirt. The eyes she lifted to his were still shadowed with uneasiness. Was he still angry with her? Was she to be punished after all?

'What we share at this moment is too precious to spoil,' Raven murmured, and as the tremors ceased, the tension began to ebb from her tired body.

The girl who had served them with ale downstairs brought water and clean linen cloths, a bottle of rum and two glasses.

'From Captain Morgan himself,' she said, her gaze dwelling sympathetically on Angelina's bruised face. Men! Not one of them could recognise that this was a lady, different from the whores who usually invaded the tavern in droves. No wonder Raven had wanted to hide her beauty from everyone—those looks would fetch a fortune in gold coin from any one of a hundred men, had they a chance to bid for her!

'Convey my thanks to him, and tell him I shall see him in the morning before I leave.'

Raven closed and locked the door behind her. He wanted no one else to disturb them. Returning to the bed, he wetted the cloth, wrung it out and laid it gently against Angelina's cheek. 'How did these come about?' he asked, transferring it to each of the scratches in turn. He had been puzzling over them ever since he first saw them.

She motioned with her hand towards the protruding nail, and he nodded in understanding. 'Sharlock underestimated your courage. You are quite the bravest young woman I have ever encountered,' he added, drying her skin with the same meticulous care, his touch light and impersonal. Nevertheless she still found herself blushing to have him minister to her—and shower her with praise.

'I was terrified,' she whispered. 'I knew he meant to kill you . . . I could not let that happen, could I?'

'You kept your wits about you more than most men would.' A dark eyebrow arched at the question. 'Better the devil you know, is that what you decided?' A familiar mocking note had crept back into his tone.

Althought she was too exhausted to retaliate in strength, she answered meaningfully, 'Perhaps I should not have screamed after all?'

'We both know what would have happened had you not. A fate as unpleasant for me as it would have been for you. I accept that I owe you my life. Shall we say it wipes out what has so far passed between us: your deliberate deception in staying on board my ship, and the given word you never intended to keep?'

'As you wish.' She was no accomplished liar. Even now, she did not know how she had managed to carry out the deception so well.

Drawing back from her, he half-filled both glasses with rum. While she stared apprehensively at hers, he drained his. He tipped the glass she held against her lips, and commanded quietly, but firmly,

'Drink it, it will help you to sleep. You will not find it unpleasant. Unless I am very much mistaken, this bottle comes from Morgan's private stock and is the best to be found outside Jamaica. I should know, I gave him the last consignment!'

The dark liquid slid effortlessly down her throat. She waited for some adverse reaction, never having tasted it before, and was pleasantly surprised at the warm glow which immediately spread through her. Raven replenished his glass and watched as she slowly finished hers. She would suffer no nightmares tonight, he mused, as she settled beneath the covers with a sigh.

'Why me?' The question came without warning. Even Angelina herself did not know what prompted her to broach the matter so boldly at this particular moment. 'There must be many other women better suited to please you than I? Willing women who would go with you wherever you chose?'

'But I want only you. The life I live is a precarious one, and it could be a very short existence, therefore I intend to make it as pleasant and satisfying as possible. Circumstances thrust this life upon me, so I intend to make the most of what I have.'

'You—You were not always a pirate?' she asked, relieved that he was not annoyed by her inquisitiveness. The sword hanging in his cabin! Was that the key to his past—his identity? She would look at it again when she returned on board.

'No.' He drained his glass before proceeding to remove first his boots, and then the wide black sash across his chest. His sword was placed beside the bed within easy reach. His knife and the pistol taken from his belt were pushed beneath the adjoining pillow. Angelina's heartbeats quickened as leather waistcoat and shirt were removed and tossed to the end of the bed.

She had only once seen a man in such a state of undress before. Raven! *Never* had she been in such déshabille in the presence of one. Her eyes lingered on the sun-tanned shoulders where small scars seared the dark skin . . . the broad chest with its mat of black curls. She wanted to reach out and draw him to her, to snatch away the mask and see the face of the man beneath, but she held back from doing so and from making the final committment which would surrender her totally into his hands—a confession of her love.

It would be her secret to bring both joy and sorrow into her life for the wonder of this new revelation was overshadowed by the shame which accompanied the knowledge that she was a willing participant in whatever happened to her after tonight. If he let her go—when he let her go, for she was still sure she would be discarded when he had tired of her, no matter how ardent his desire at present—she would not be able to return to England. That life was forever lost to her. How could she face Edgar and her friends and admit that she loved a pirate, and wanted him to make love to her and sail away with her to some remote place where they could be alone! Her love made her an outcast from decent society, and she must accept that.

Raven settled himself alongside her, staring down at her with thoughtful eyes. He sensed that she had somehow withdrawn from him.

'Put your arms round me. Pretend I am Edgar Sarandon if you like,' he said in a low, fierce whisper as he reached for her.

He had misunderstood her long silence! He thought she was thinking of Edgar and regretting what had been left behind. The glitter of London society—the wealth with which she had been surrounded and grown accustomed to since the prosperity of her father's business. An ideal marriage!

Her lips were crushed beneath his; everything was blotted from her mind. Obediently she locked her hands behind his head, her fingers against the crisp black hair curling there, and she tried to envisage Edgar's face and recall his kisses. She could do neither. He was part of the world she had chosen to abandon. She would never think of him again, she vowed.

'You are mine, Angelina.' His fingers entwined themselves in the thick mane of red hair as his mouth explored hers with the expertise of a practised lover, until her being clamoured for the satisfaction only his domination of her body could provide. The hand caressing her burned her skin, and she abandoned herself totally to the fires and the wildness mounting unchallenged inside her. She was committed now—she could have no regrets. Besides, how could something which made her feel so alive, be so wrong?

She had never loved Edgar, she knew that now, but had Raven not abducted her, she would have married him, borne his children and remained faithful to him for the rest of her life. She would never have known moments like this—when she was possessed by unbridled passion. What did it matter if Raven did not love her? He desired her with an intensity few men ever experienced, and those who did, lavished it on their horses, or a favoured mistress. That was what she would be—his mistress! Never his wife. Sharing his bed, but not his name. His property!

For a moment her strict upbringing, the rules of conduct she had set for herself when first she entered London society—and scrupulously maintained even after her betrothal to Edgar—rose up to confront her with the enormity of what she had done . . . only to be banished for ever as Raven's kisses rendered her incapable of all thought other than the exquisite pleasure which now engulfed her.

It was Raven who broke the spell, drawing himself up on one elbow beside her to survey her flushed cheeks, the soft mouth still quivering from the intensity of his demanding kisses. He had accepted that she was shocked from Sharlock's brutal treatment of her; in need of sympathy, and comfort, of tenderness such as he had never shown her before. Even so, he had expected some slight resistance to his embrace—some show of modesty directed against the boldness of his caresses. Yet she lay passive beneath him—unresisting. No, that was not true. Not passive, for he had felt the response from her lips, and become increasingly aware of an awakening in her body. He had roused her! If he took her now, she might well hate him for it. She never knew the effort it cost him to curtail his desire and end the madness which had momentarily possessed him.

'You can't appear in the streets in that shirt,' he said with a half-smile, and pulled the offending material together to cover the rise of her firm breasts. 'I'll find you another, or I'll have more men to fight over you.' The flush of colour which rose in her cheeks pleased him, although he would never have told her so. He could hurt and embarrass her so easily with words, he realised, at last accepting that, despite the man's world in which she had been living for the past year or so, she had kept her innocence. The fragile innocence of a perfect English rose. She would blossom beneath his tutorship, learn to enjoy the gifts with which God had endowed her, but at the same time he hoped she would retain the simplicity which was so appealing—especially now as she lay staring up at him with wide eyes, uncertain of him—of herself. Perhaps with her he could salvage something from the worthless existence he had been enduring for the past four years—settle down and forget all thoughts of further vengeance . . .

It was the mask which frightened her still, he thought. Should he remove it? Not yet. For a while longer he wanted to enjoy this new, unexpected surrender on her part. If she discovered his secret—and while he intended to take every precaution to avoid telling her until the last moment—she would hate him again, and fear him as the monster who had plucked her from the safety of Edgar Sarandon's loving arms. She said she loved him . . . Had she lied? She was certainly not averse to a few untruths here and there.

'I warn you I shall be a jealous lover, so take care where your eyes alight,' he murmured warningly. 'Despite this change—albeit a welcome one in you—I am not of a mind to forget there is a temper to match that red hair, and a devious woman's mind lurking behind that innocent expression.'

'Did you not want me a docile creature, obedient to your every whim?' Angelina asked with a faint smile. She did not mind his suspicions or that he had no comprehension of how she felt about him—in time he would discover that she was quite content to remain with him. For ever, if he would have her. If only such a miracle were possible!

The rum had made her so sleepy that she could hardly keep her eyes open, and he grinned amusedly as she smothered a yawn.

'I see my company is boring you already.'

'Are—Are you intending to stay—stay here all night?'

'Beside you, but awake . . . Just in case. Go to sleep. You are quite safe.'

She had never felt less safe with his hard body pressed close against her—never less in control of herself. Snuggling well beneath the bedclothes, she turned on her side away from him. She felt him stretch and flex his muscles. Within minutes, she was asleep.

*   *   *

It was light when she awoke again, alone. She quickly sat up, fighting down the fear which made her heart race unsteadily. Across the bottom of the bed was a clean silk shirt, and pinned to it a note. In a bold, flourishing hand, Raven had written, *'I am waiting for you downstairs. Do not make me wait too long.'* It was a command to dress and join him—or he would come and fetch her! Why should she linger in this drab room when she could be with him in minutes? she thought, flinging back the covers. Peeling off the torn shirt, she put on the one provided, splashed cold water on to her face to rouse her more fully—and winced as she dried it, touching the bruised places she had forgotten were there. What a sight she must look! She had no mirror to see herself, no brush to tidy her hair.

There were faint red marks on her wrists where the ropes had cut into her soft skin, but luckily the lace ruffles of the long sleeves hid them sufficiently. The shirt fitted her well, she found, as she tucked it into her trousers and pulled on her boots. Raven had a good eye. How would he greet her this morning? As the gentle, compassionate man who had held her the night before and soothed away her fears? Or the arrogant, ruthless pirate who had stolen her from the *White Swan*, determined to subdue her to his will? There was only one way to find out.

A man below gave a long, loud whistle of admiration as she descended the stairs. The buzz of conversation dwindled as all eyes swivelled to focus on the slender figure who stood hesitating on the last step, and then resumed again, glances being averted as Raven rose from the table where he sat with Henry Morgan, and extended his hand. She need no further encouragement than that simple gesture to hurry to his side. Before everyone he was proclaiming what he had stated the night before: that she was his woman! Not to be touched; to be treated with respect. Not one head was raised as she passed the tables to join him.

'I did not expect you so soon. You were sleeping like a babe when I left not half an hour ago,' he said. Pulling her against him, he kissed her soundly on the lips—as much a warning for the men who were near by as for her. Even if she wanted to, she could not ask help from any of them now that they knew whose property she was. He had ensured their good behaviour—and bolted the door of her self-made prison behind her. If the whole of Tortuga did not already know who she was, they would before the morning was out!

'Your note had an impatient air about it,' she replied, meekly allowing him to settle her in a chair alongside him.

'Sharlock did not deserve such a quick death for marking such a lovely face,' Henry Morgan declared, staring at the scratches and bruises which showed painfully clear in the strong light. The bruise on Angelina's cheek had begun to turn yellow and blue, and as she raised a hand self-consciously to touch it, Raven saw the smudges on her wrists, and his mouth tightened.

'We are in agreement over that. Are you hungry, angel, or shall we go on board directly?'

'I would like to leave here . . .' He nodded, understanding her discomfort in such a place. For him it served a purpose when he was bored or in need of a woman. He hoped he would be neither in the months ahead.

'We shall take our leave of you then, Henry,' Raven said, and they shook hands warmly.

'You will not reconsider and come with me?' Henry asked, and then shook his head as his eyes considered

Angelina. 'Perhaps not. I can't blame you for preferring such delightful company. I am desolate you are leaving so soon, madam.' He took her hand and touched her fingers to his lips. 'Take good care of Raven; you will not find the like of him again.'

'I was told you were a cut-throat pirate, a disgrace to your country, Captain Morgan. I shall be able to tell people you are not,' she said with a smile. To her astonishment, the whole room exploded with laughter, and loudest of all was the throaty roar of the man in front of her.

'Take her away, Raven laddie, before I succumb to the wench's compliments.' He pulled a handkerchief from his coat and dabbed at his wet eyes, and fell back into his chair still convulsed with laughter.

'What did I say that was so funny?' Angelina demanded indignantly, as with Raven's hand tight about her arm she was hustled out into the street. He, too, had found her remarks amusing, she saw, looking up into the masked face. The eyes looking down at her were brimming with mirth. 'I found him quite the gentleman. Mr Forrester, my captain aboard the White Swan, told me he was a black-hearted rogue with no regard for womanhood, and that he allowed his men to loot and torture without restraint upon them. I saw no evidence to confirm any of his words.'

'My dear child, Henry can be the epitome of an English gentleman when he so chooses,' Raven replied coolly.

'As you can,' she interrupted.

'You would not think him such a fine specimen if you had seen him at Maracaibo a few months back, or raiding a Spanish settlement along the coast. Then he is the devil incarnate . . . He has to be to control the men with him. He is no worse and no better than the rest of us.' Her words were ignored. He had no intention of enlightening her about his own background, she realised. The sword was her best chance to discover something—anything—about him. 'The Spaniards look fine gentlemen, too—from a distance—but once in their hands as a prisoner, any man—or woman for that matter—is better off dead.'

'Does he really have letters of marque from the British Government?'

'He does. As I do. We have their permission, and their blessing, to seek out Spanish ships and destroy them . . . to lay waste to their settlements . . . to free the slaves they force into bondage to work their silver mines. I take great pleasure in depriving them of their wealth—which so many poor devils have died to obtain for them.'

'How horrible.' Angelina shivered, and then as a sudden thought struck her, she looked up at him with a coldness in her eyes which took him aback.

'Do your letters of marque also include ships showing the Sarandon pennant? Since when did Edgar become a Spaniard?'

He threw her an angry look, and for a good while they walked in silence. Sometimes she found she had almost to run to keep up with his long strides. In the light of day she discovered that Tortuga was not the kind of place she would have liked to stay for any length of time. The streets were littered with rubbish from vendors who hawked their wares from rickety wooden stalls. Fruit, vegetables, leatherware and bolts of cloth. Seamen with bold eyes surveyed every woman that passed, often making lewd comments or offering an invitation. Painted women wandered along the harbour, offering themselves without one iota of shame for an hour of pleasure, mingling with dirty-faced, bare-footed urchins who imitated their swaying gait from a safe distance.

Many eyes followed the tall masked man and the slim girl who hurried at his side, clothed as a boy, long red hair streaming out behind her in the wind. By the time they had reached Raven's ship, she was out of breath and burning with embarrassment from the stares directed towards her.

'Is—Is my face a sight?' Angelina touched her cheek gingerly. It still felt very tender. Raven paused at the bottom of the gangplank to hear her out. 'Do I look very bruised? People have been staring at me so rudely.'

'They probably think I have beaten you for being disobedient,' he chuckled infuriatingly, and ushered her on board. 'I suppose you want to find Charity, and assure yourself that she is unharmed?' She nodded, sensing that he wanted her below decks and out of the way as quickly as possible. 'Very well.'

She found Charity seated in the cabin they had previously shared, sewing a piece of bright blue material, as unruffled by her surroundings and all that had happened to her—including the fact that she was as much a prisoner as Angelina—as if she had been in the sitting-room in England whiling away a few hours until the evening meal.

'Angelina, my dear child, what has happened to you?' She came out of her chair, a hand against her mouth as the girl entered and came close enough for her failing eyesight to take in the discolorations on her face. 'Surely he—Raven—surely he did not . . . do this to you?' she whispered. 'No gentleman would mark a lady so.'

'Neither manners nor fine clothes make a gentleman, Charity,' Angelina replied, hugging her in relief to find her safe and well. Raven had been so angry at their attack on Stumpy that she was not sure what kind of punishment—if any—he intended for them. It seemed that neither was to be reprimanded for what had happened. 'Why you should think he is a man of breeding is beyond me . . . but you do, don't you? You have thought so since we first came on board.'

'Sometimes . . .' The woman's face wrinkled into a disturbed frown. 'Sometimes there is a familiarity about him . . . I am mistaken, of course. Whoever he reminds me of, I cannot remember either name or face. My poor memory.'

'I doubt if you have ever met Raven mingling with London society,' Angelina said, smiling at such a thought. She could just imagine the reaction of the women about him at the sight of those broad shoulders and suntanned skin, the cloak of mystery that surrounded his identity. He would have them all at his feet—and earn the enmity of every man present. That would not unduly concern him, she decided. She had seen that he was a man who could take care of himself under the most difficult of circumstances. 'But I think it is time we tried to discover what manner of man holds us prisoner . . .' What manner of man I love, she almost said, and stopped herself in time. She did not want Charity to swoon at such horrifying news.

'I do not think we should do anything to antagonise him, child,' Charity answered quickly, not liking the look in the girl's eyes. 'We are well treated, and he asks nothing from us. Soon Lord Sarandon will pay our ransoms and we shall be on our way home. You will forget this whole unpleasant episode. Think how wonderful it will be to get back to England—to the house and your friends.'

Oh, Charity, if only you knew, Angelina thought, not

daring to speak a word lest she gave herself away. The woman had completely forgotten the first night on board, when they had dined with the pirate captain and he had bluntly told them both why he had boarded the *White Swan*. She believed they would soon be free.

'Stumpy is not badly injured, you know.' She changed the subject in her usual erratic way, and would have sat down again to continue with her sewing if Angelina had not prevented it. 'What is it? Do you want to see him? He has a rock for a head, you know. He told me so himself. He said he hardly felt the blow. So nice about it, he was . . . He made me feel so ashamed.'

'Charity, I need your help to look in Raven's cabin. There is a sword there, with an inscription on it in Latin. You can translate it for me. It is very, very important to me. Please help me?' she urged. 'The captain is on deck. We shall be a few minutes only, and he will never know we were there.'

'Very well, but I don't like it . . . A sword, you say?'

'Yes. Quickly now.'

Angelina did not breathe easily again until the door of Raven's cabin had closed behind them. She could hear him shouting orders on the deck above as the ship slipped out on the tide. He would be occupied for some while yet. Her eyes lingered for a moment on the shoreline, as Tortuga gradually became no more than a few white distant dots, her thoughts flying back to the tavern and the moments they had shared which might never be repeated. He had not seemed over-anxious to assert his authority this morning. Was he so sure of himself, and of her, that he treated her so casually? Did he think she would run to him if he but crooked his finger in her direction? She knew she would. She would not be able to help herself. She wanted the strength of his arms about her again, giving her sanctuary from the outside world. With his kisses, she would forget the shameful bargain she had made and was now prepared to keep so willingly.

'Is this what you were talking about?' Charity enquired. She had located the sword, and stood peering at it closely. 'Fine workmanship . . . It reminds me . . .'

'Not now, Charity, please.' Angelina did not want her going off into the realms of fantasy again, or delving into the past, searching for someone who had once owned a similar weapon. She wanted the Latin inscription translated. 'Can you read what is on it?'

'My eyes are not what they were, you know that. Read it for me.'

' "*Quo fata vocant*", I think.'

' "*Whither the fates call.*" ' The answer came without hesitation. 'Now where have I seen that before?'

'You are probably confusing it with someone else's family motto,' Angelina replied quietly. '*Whither the fates call.*' Was it possible that it was Raven's motto? That would mean he was indeed a gentleman, and not a low-born adventurer who had taken to the sea in order to line his pockets with Spanish gold. And to attack Edgar's ships, she reminded herself again. She must never let herself forget that. In business, men made many enemies, and Edgar was no exception. Was Raven a seaman whom he had dismissed? A business rival who had run foul of him? How was she to find out?

If Raven had not halted at the door at that moment to speak with one of the crew, neither of them would have known of his presence outside. As it was, the sound of his voice sent Angelina into a near panic. The last thing she wanted was him to find her in his cabin— deliberately spying on him—and so ruin the truce which was in effect between them. Grabbing Charity by the arm, she dragged her into the smaller bedroom and closed the door, but inched it open again just enough to be able to see out into the cabin.

She had not expected him so soon. What if he came into the bedroom? There was nowhere for them to hide in the small area . . . She watched, her heart in her mouth, as he entered and locked the door after him. He removed his waistcoat, and tossing it across a chair, poured himself a glass of wine. He drank it as he stood staring out of the open window, apparently lost in deep thought. She felt her nerves begin to grow as taut as a bowstring, and prayed for someone to come and ask him to return to the deck so that they could safely escape from his predicament.

He went as if to pour himself another, then changed his mind and sat down behind the huge mahogany desk where his maps were spread. He was tired, she realised, as he leant his head against the back of the padded leather chair. Of course, he had not slept the night before. She felt as if her heart suddenly missed a beat with shock. Raven had reached up to the silken covering over his face, and pulled it off with a heavy sigh.

Where were the scars? She could not see a single mark! It was a strong face, with high cheekbones and a straight, perfect nose. Not a blemish on the heavily bronzed skin. Why—he was handsome! Yet he chose to hide behind an ugly mask. There were tiny white lines on each side of his eyes, which looked larger now and framed by coal-black lashes. Charity, not understanding the look of amazement on her face, eased herself to the crack, and peered through.

The cry that she uttered brought Raven out of his chair like a wild animal springing towards a helpless prey. Before Angelina could move or think, the door was flung open and steely fingers fastened over her arm, dragging her from her hiding-place. She opened her mouth to speak, and then saw he was not even looking at her—all his attention was centred on Charity, who was swaying unsteadily as she gazed into the brown features.

'Now I remember . . .' Her voice was hardly audible. Angelina winced as Raven's fingers tightened painfully over her skin, yet he seemed unaware of her discomfort, or did not care. 'The sword . . . the inscription . . . of course . . . over the fireplace at Tall Chimneys.'

Angelina gasped, the pain forgotten. 'But that is —Edgar's family home, in Gloucestershire.'

'Jason's home, my dear,' Charity corrected with a smile. 'Only he ever had the feeling for it that it deserved.'

'Damn you, Charity,' Raven ejaculated harshly. 'I thought your memory was lost to you!'

'Who are you?' Angelina breathed, a terrible fear growing inside her. It could not be possible. If it was, it meant that she was in love with a . . . She could not even consider such a thing! 'Charity, for the love of heaven, tell me who he is?'

'Why, Lord Sarandon, Angelina. My own dear Jason, come back to me! He is not dead.'

'No, I am very much alive—and seeking justice,' he replied in tones of ice. 'You, of all people, should understand why.'

'Oh, I do . . .' Charity's voice trailed away, and he stepped forward to catch her up in his arms as she fainted.

CHAPTER
SEVEN

CHARITY LAY propped up against a mound of brightly covered cushions in a huge chair which almost hid her small frame. She sipped the brandy Raven had given her when she recovered consciousness, but so far had not spoken. She appeared to be in a trance-like state, although Angelina suspected that she was fully aware of the two other people in the cabin with her.

Raven had perched himself on the edge of his desk. He had consumed two large glasses of rum from the decanter at his side while she lay in her faint. He had not spoken, either, and that was as frightening for Angelina as the discovery of his identity. His eyes were like grey flints as they considered first one woman and then the other. The mouth was a taut line, rigid with anger. He would no doubt have preferred his little game to have continued for a good while longer. Until he had got her into his bed, perhaps!

She felt hot with shame to think that she had abandoned herself to the arms of a murderer. Jason Sarandon, Edgar's elder brother, who had so callously raped and murdered his pretty little ward when she had repulsed his advances. Had he thought that his good looks could get him any woman he wanted? Drusilla Ansley had been the exception. She had spurned him, and paid a terrible price for the rejection. And this was the man she loved. How could she, knowing what he was? She tried to analyse her feelings at that moment, but her mind was too confused and pounding with questions.

Justice! He had said that he was seeking justice. Against whom, and for what? He was the murderer —the fugitive from justice! And Charity knew why. What did she know? What was locked away in her mind? Had the sight of his unmasked face restored what she had lost on the night of her accident, or had parts only returned further to distort half-truths and innuendoes?

She realised that Raven was standing before her, holding out a glass of rum. She shook her head. She wanted nothing from him.

'Take it—you look as if you need it.' It was an order, not a request, and against her will, she complied. The look in his eyes gave her the impression that he would force the contents down her throat if she did not. Returning to the desk, he folded his arms over his chest, his mouth growing bleak again.

'Did you have to open Pandora's box?' he said heavily. 'You have no idea what you have done, you little fool!'

'How dare you try to attach any blame for this to me!' she flung back, stung by his scornful words. 'You are the one who has been practising a deception, hiding behind that mask because you were afraid that Charity would recognise you and denounce you for the murderer you are!'

'She will never do that,' came the confident reply, and she felt herself stiffen in fear. 'And the mask was for the benefit of neither of you. Unless I am safe at home, I prefer to keep my face covered.'

'How will you stop her? You—You would not hurt her? You could not . . . She is a harmless old woman!' she cried aghast, dreading to think what loathsome secrets he harboured that made the deception necessary.

'You have made her remember the past—the ugly past—and that may have caused her more pain than anything I could ever say or do,' Raven snapped, his eyes beginning to smoulder with anger. Damn her for her inquisitiveness! His carefully-laid plans had all been for nothing. He could have slept last night instead of lying beside her, thinking how it would be for them both in the months ahead. He would have denied her nothing. Now the loathing in those green depths told him that the dream was destroyed. He felt like striking her. And then she turned to stare at Charity, and the sunlight fell across the mark on her cheek. Instantly he was ashamed of such a thought. He was no Sharlock! He had lived too much among rabble. The return of Charity's memory might well deprive him of ever being free of the life he now led. He wished that Edgar was with them so that he could put his hands round his brother's skinny neck and squeeze every last breath from his body.

'You blame me? I have killed no one! How many more have there been since that poor girl—your ward?' Angelina cried.

Raven came away from the desk and dragged her up against him, imprisoning her wrists with his hands. His face, close to hers, was terrible in its fury. 'Take care with your words, Angelina. Remember where you are. This is not England, but my ship, and I am master on board. Your master, whenever I choose. Do you hear me? Understand what I am saying?' He shook her roughly, and she cried out as a pain seared her head at the jolt he gave her. He was like a man possessed. Had he been like this with Drusilla on the night she tried to send him away?

'You—You cannot expect me to . . . I will not!' The

thought of his arms about her, his lips on hers, was suddenly obnoxious. He could not expect her to go through with their bargain now, after what she had learnt. But he did! She saw it written on his face. 'Now I understand why you abducted me—the true reason. You had never seen me; you somehow heard I was to wed Edgar; you hate him. You would do anything to hurt him, you told me so yourself! You took his first sweetheart from him . . . forced yourself on her when she refused your advances! But you will not take me from him.' She flung back her head, defiance blazing out of her face as she confronted him. 'Nor will I suffer your vile hands on me.'

'They did not displease you last night,' Raven snapped, and she gasped in horror, her cheeks growing pale.

'If you touch me again, I—I shall kill you,' she vowed, hating him for confronting her with the truth at such a time.

'I suggest you consider that threat very carefully before we reach land again. Your discovery of who I am changes nothing. I still intend to have you. If you break your word to me again, I shall not hesitate to use force.' She knew he meant every word. 'My patience was at an end, Angelina, because of your damned meddling. Never mind!' He rounded on Charity, who was watching them with a growing comprehension in her expression. She smiled as Angelina tore herself free from Raven's grasp, and knelt beside her.

'Charity, are you all right? I am so sorry . . . I didn't know . . . How could I? Have I caused you pain?'

'More pain than you can ever imagine, and not only for her,' Raven remarked behind her. 'And you have stirred up a hornets' nest that cannot be controlled. From this moment, none of our lives will ever be the same again. All due to you, Angelina. How like a woman to poke her nose into matters which don't concern her! I shall be on deck, if my company suddenly becomes acceptable to you.'

Angelina did not turn round as he left the cabin, but the slamming of the door made her wince. He blamed her! How could she change the course of their lives? He talked in riddles, perhaps seeking to confuse her further and cover his own black deed in more mystery. Charity was the answer . . . but when she turned back to question her, the woman was asleep, her face free of all anxiety, as peaceful as a saint. She did not have the heart to disturb her, but settled herself in a chair again to await her revival.

Her head reeled with so many unanswered questions that she felt quite giddy. Jason Sarandon was the mysterious masked pirate Raven. How he had escaped from England she did not know, only that he had somehow faked his own death and then taken to the high seas —and a life of piracy. But how was it possible for him to have letters of marque from the British Government? They would never have issued them to him in his own name, so what other identity did he have? What powerful friends did he retain from the past to keep his whereabouts a secret and to protect him from the justice he has escaped four years before?

He could answer her questions as well as Charity. He owed it to her, and it would save the poor woman more anguish. Why had she not been more frightened when she saw Jason's face again? Was it not he who had struck her down when she discovered him leaving Drusilla's bedroom after the brutal attack? She had spoken his name as though he were someone precious to her— almost like a son. She had been with the Sarandon family since both sons were quite young, first as their governess, then companion to the young girl Jason had brought into his home as his ward. But surely, after the way he had treated her, she would hate him?

Was she in her right mind—or had the shock of seeing a dead man come to life sent her over the edge of the abyss into the dark world of total confusion, so that times and places were muddled . . . people the same as when she had last seen them, even after the passing of many years? She had given Angelina the impression that she did not have the slightest idea she was on board a ship . . .

Angelina laid her lips gently against a cold cheek before leaving the cabin. Raúl sketched a saucy salute before her as she appeared on deck, and jerked his head towards the upper deck where Raven stood behind the helm, taking it for granted that it was his captain she had come to find.

'Thank you,' she said stiffly.

'So you have decided that my company is not so odious after all?' Raven remarked, as she stopped some distance from him, but well in his line of vision. A lazy, mocking smile played around the lean mouth as he gave her his full attention, noting by the coldness of her expression and the fire burning in her eyes, that she had come prepared to do battle. 'Do not vex me, Angelina, I am in no mood for it,' he warned.

'I demand to know where you are taking us!'

'When you first came on board my ship, I told you that you were in no position to demand anything from me.' The wheel spun under his hands, and she felt the ship begin to turn.

'You have changed course. Where are we going? What harm is there in telling me?'

'Home,' he said with a brief shrug of his shoulders. 'we are heading home. I live in a very charming house on an island paradise within easy reach of the island of Jamaica. You will like it.'

'I shall hate it,' she retorted. The truth about him had washed the love-dust from her eyes. What a blind fool she had been to be deceived by his charm. Poor Drusilla had also been caught in the same trap, and when she had attempted to escape, had suffered the ultimate penalty for her folly. Would she? She ran her hands up and down her arms as if chilled by the wind, and Raven frowned at the action. 'What do you intend to do with Charity? Give her to Stumpy as part of his share of the booty?'

'There are many women servants whom you will find willing to chatter with you daily about the trifling things women always seem to talk about for hours on end, but I thought Charity's company would help you to adjust to your new life in your new home. As for giving her to Stumpy . . . she could do worse. In his way, he is rather fond of her.'

'She is not well . . . She is in need of care, medical care,' she protested, disgusted by his lack of concern.

'She shall have the best there is. Does that set your mind at rest?'

'Why should you care for her? She can identify you to the authorities—as I can.' Angelina froze as the eyes Raven focused on her blazed suddenly.

'Don't even think it, angel. On my island, which I incidentally own—lock, stock and barrel—I am in sole control. Nothing happens that I do not know about . . . Nothing is said behind my back that does not come to my ears, eventually. I shall know what you do every moment of the day—where you are every minute . . .'

'You mean I shall be watched—spied on—by your

. . . hirelings.' The life he painted for her made her feel quite ill. She would be no more than a chattel at his beck and call. No will of her own—her sole purpose in life, to obey his every wish.

'It need not be like that,' he told her quietly, aware of the thoughts racing through her mind. She had such expressive eyes that she could hide nothing from him, although she seemed unaware of the extent to which she revealed her innermost thoughts. He had lain beside her in the tavern and gazed deep into them—and known that she had wanted him to make love to her, as intensely as he had wanted it himself. An hour ago he had cursed her to hell, and Charity and her blasted memory—and himself for not recognising that her woman's curiosity had to get the better of her at some time . . . and he had known such anger that none of his crew had dared approach him when he first appeared. It was abating now, and he knew he must somehow try to win her trust again, or lose her. He had threatened force and, at that time, he had meant what he said, but the idea was now so repugnant to him that he knew he could never go through with it. If he was drunk enough, or she inflamed him beyond restraint with her sarcasm, his natural instincts might be overcome . . . his desire for her might take precedence over everything . . . But he doubted it. The memory of Drusilla was still too vivid a nightmare.

'Will you tell me nothing?' Angelina cried in distraction.

'The past does not concern you. Only the present, and what lies ahead. A pleasant future for us both if you are a sensible young woman.'

'A pleasant future,' she repeated bitterly. 'The mistress of a murderer! I would rather be dead.'

'Perhaps I should take you below and remind you how

it was between us last night.' His eyes gleamed wickedly, challenging her words. She could never take her own life, and he knew it—not while Charity was still his prisoner. No flowery adjectives could change their situation: they were both his prisoners!

'You flatter yourself, sir.' She had only one defence against the memory of that night—to attack him in every way she could—to wound him—to hurt him as he had hurt her. 'You are not to be compared with your brother!'

The taunt struck home. Raven's eyes narrowed to angry slits of fire. The smile which deepened his mouth was not a pleasant one. He was seeing her as she had been the night before, she realised—half naked!

'I would have wagered a chest full of gold that you still had your innocence.' He gave a hollow laugh. 'Thank you for opening my eyes. Now I know the kind of woman I am dealing with! Get below, you are distracting my men!' he suddenly roared at her, and she turned and fled, afraid of his devilish features—afraid of the consequences of her stupidity.

She was not sure if she could handle the storm she had unleashed upon herself. She would tell him it was not true . . . that she had never allowed Edgar even to slip his hand inside her bodice, though it was not for the want of his trying! He had only kissed her . . . But would he believe her? It should not matter what he thought, but it did. Why, oh, why could she not kill this love which lingered inside her despite all she had discovered? It would surely destroy her—if Raven did not do so first!

The days that followed were the most miserable Angelina had ever experienced. Charity's strange moods, which varied without warning, caused her great distress. Sometimes the woman was perfectly lucid and knew her, and the conversations between them would be quite normal. But there were frightening occasions when she lapsed into the past and addressed Angelina as Drusilla. It was then that she discovered more about the dead girl then than anyone had ever told her before. Her favourite flowers, the clothes she preferred to wear, of her love for Edgar. She had been courted by many, but had never selected a husband. Had her guardian kept them all at bay, hoping one day to have her for himself? Angelina often wondered.

Charity sat in a chair in her small cabin, mumbling and remembering in low monosyllables. Always Jason Sarandon was the one she talked of most often—he had obviously been her favourite. Edgar had always maintained that his elder brother had overshadowed him to the day he went to his watery death. His supposed watery death! Jason had always done everything so well. She remembered the bitterness in Edgar's voice as he spoke of the dead man one night when he had had too much to drink. When she had broached on the subject again, the next day, he had flatly refused to be drawn.

Jason could ride like the wind. Jason could handle a sword better than any man in London, and had proved it many a time in duels. Jason was handsome enough to have any woman he chose, just by looking at her! Jason could handle pistols as if he had been born with one in each hand. Jason . . . Jason . . . Always Jason!

Poor Edgar, he had indeed been a mere shadow beside his brother. Now Angelina could understand much better why he had turned out to be weak of character, a gambler, at times drinking far in excess of his limited capacity. Jason had been strong; never gambled away his money when it could be invested and put to good use; drank sometimes to excess, but could hold his liquor.

Edgar had loved Drusilla, but what chance did he stand against such a paragon of virtue? Yet by some miracle, she had loved him back, and Jason's courtship had been rejected.

'A little more, if you please, my dear,' Charity murmured, holding out her empty glass. Stumpy had made it a habit to bring a bottle of Madeira with the main meal that Angelina always took with her, as she did every other one . . . She left the cabin only to sleep. She had not been up on deck since they sailed from Tortuga, and she was feeling the strain, but she could not bring herself to face Raven's scornful eyes. He blamed her for what had happened, and he was right—but he, too, should accept some of the blame. Had he not been masked, concealing his identity from her, she would never have gone to his cabin.

Would she have fallen in love with him had she known from the beginning that he was Jason Sarandon, she had often asked herself as she lay abed unable to sleep. Could she have ignored the charm of the man, the desire for her he had never bothered to hide, the trouble he had gone to in order to snatch her from the *White Swan*? He had made her feel a woman—wanted—even Edgar had never succeeded in doing that . . . not in the way Raven did.

With a smile, Angelina rose and fetched the decanter and poured Charity another full glass. She would begin to doze soon, and she herself would go on deck for some badly-needed fresh air. It was quite dark, so she hoped to escape the notice of Raven if he was at the wheel.

He came many times to the cabin to see Charity. She knew him every time, greeted him like a dear friend and was, in return, treated like one. Much as she wanted to believe otherwise, Angelina was forced to admit that they were extremely fond of each other. Considering what he had done to her, she thought Charity had an exceptionally generous heart.

Stumpy was the same with her. Angelina he practically ignored. Somewhat haltingly, she had made apologies for striking him, unable to bear his dour looks and sour silence for more than three days. He had shrugged, told her he had been hit harder before, and went on with what he was doing. His concern for Charity did not extend to the pale-faced young woman hovering in the background.

She told herself it did not matter what he thought of her, how off-hand his attitude was towards her. He was nothing but a pirate, and she would survive his rudeness. She told herself the same thing when Raven bade her no more than the courtesies of the day, reserving all his attention, his gentle tones and helpful manner for Charity alone. When she was in the room, Angelina might not have existed.

On one occasion he told her she was free to walk on deck after dark. Why not during the day? When, of course, she questioned such a high-handed order, the curt retort came back that she was too much of a distraction for his men to parade herself in daylight. She had thought to show him that she would not be ordered about like a chattel and remained below, but as the days had slipped by, she came to accept she was hurting no one but herself.

Stumpy came to take their plates, gazed fondly at the woman in the chair whose eyes were slowly closing, gently took the glass from her lax fingers, and left again without a word. Angelina waited until she was sure

Charity was sound asleep, tucked the blanket across her lap more firmly into place, and tiptoed out.

Until the watch called out, she had no idea it was so late—midnight! The deck was deserted except for one or two men leaning over the side, talking in low tones. She passed on the other side of them and found herself a spot where the wind was in her face. How good it felt! She breathed deeply of the cool night air and stretched cramped limbs, relaxed against the rigging to marvel at the twinkling jewel-like stars above her. She knew most of them by heart; her father and Mr Forrester had made sure of that. The moon was full, illuminating the whole of the maindeck and the quarterdeck, where a pirate stood at the wheel. Not tall enough for Raven, she noticed in relief. She slept badly these nights, which was how she knew that he usually took the wheel throughout the hours of darkness and slept part of the day. She would hear his footsteps pass her door at night and return again just after first light. She was troubled by her own conscience and the pain she had unwittingly brought to Charity. What devil haunted him that he could not rest, either? The ghost of Drusilla Ansley?

Never before had she felt so alone and troubled in herself. Everything she had now at this moment had come from him—except for the boy's clothes tucked away in the chest in her cabin. And that was the way it would continue to be. She would be reliant on him even for the food she ate! What had happened to her fighting spirit? She had sailed the high seas in command of her father's ships and revelled in the new world opening up to her. Not so much in the power she had been able to wield, but in the achievement she—a mere woman —had made. She knew that her friends thought she was mad, and many pitied Edgar because his betrothed should so callously desert him, but while her father was alive he had always come first, and she did not regret it. She was young; she could marry at any time . . . she could have married, she corrected her thoughts with a frown. Raven had made it impossible for her to hold her head up again in decent society. What man would want to take her as his wife when he discovered she had been the mistress of a bloodthirsty buccaneer?

'What are you doing on deck at this time of night?' Raven demanded close behind her, and she started violently.

'I—I could not sleep, so I came out for some air. I have had precious little these past days.' She did not turn to look at him, conscious of tears on the brink of being shed. The sight of them would surely give him the impression that his ungentlemanly treatment of her was having the desired effect.

'That is your own fault entirely. Your cabin door is not locked.' She felt his arm brush hers as he moved past her, and, slight though the contact was, a tingle of pleasure ran through her. She tried to turn away, but was caught and held fast. In the bright moonlight he could clearly see the tears brimming in her green eyes, and an oath exploded under his breath. 'Charity—is she all right?'

She swallowed hard, trying to compose herself, and nodded.

'The Madeira that Stumpy brings her always sends her off to sleep quite quickly. But then you know of her weakness for it, don't you?' Her tone was bitter because he had shared more with Charity than Angelina herself, who considered the old woman her closest friend since the death of her father. There was a tiredness in her voice, too, which Raven did not miss. Releasing her, he leaned back against the rigging, considering the way the moonlight softened the brightness of the red tresses cascading over her shoulders.

She had on one of the dresses he had given her, of palest blue silk, which did full justice, in his estimation, to her neat waist and the full curve of her breasts. But she was not wearing a single piece of the jewellery he had also provided. A gesture meant to show him that she still did not accept him, he mused, without making comment.

'I've known her a great many years longer than you have,' he acknowledged at last, aware of her growing uneasy beneath his scrutiny. 'She came to the house of my father in Gloucestershire when Edgar and I were mere boys. After his death, she was so much a part of our family that I let her stay. I could not envisage the days without her scolding me for some misdemeanour or other, even though I was well past the age when I would accept it. Are you growing bored, Angelina?'

'No.' Charity was all that concerned her these days. Besides, what did it matter where they ended up? Her position would remain the same. His prisoner now, and his mistress the moment he chose to assert his domination over her. She had been expecting it before this. If he was hoping that the long days in her cabin with only Charity—lucid or otherwise—to converse with would temper if not break her, he was right. She had taken to talking to herself at night as she lay in bed, reciting the parts of a ship, talking to a non-existent dressmaker of the gowns she wished to have made for when she next attended a court function; but even these things had been a last show of defiance, and had proved futile. If she did not talk sensibly with someone soon, she would go off her head! She was willing to talk with anyone

—anyone at all—except the man who stood beside her, whose eyes had not left her face for one instant.

Raven's first instincts when he saw her were to go direct to the wheel and relieve the man there; to let her be miserable alone. He knew that by now she must be aware of how alone and friendless she was. It was not the way he had intended the journey home would be, not after her acceptance of him at the tavern. He envisaged days when she would enjoy being with him at the wheel, nights when they dined together and talked, and she grew more at ease in his company, accepting the hunger in him and not fearing it. Nor that which he knew lingered in her. He had seen her, wanted her and taken her for himself. Not until after he had achieved this—did he readily admit to himself—would he have to woo and win her, or use other methods. She was no woman of easy virtue to fall into his arms when showered with gifts, or threatened with dire consequences if she did not.

He did not believe she had belonged to his brother. There was none of Edgar's brashness which would surely have rubbed off on her had she been as close to him as she wanted him to believe. Her words had been meant to hold him at bay, and they had succeeded. He was shocked at his own vulnerability, that the thought of her being touched by another could rouse such anger in him. He did not love her, he desired her—or so he told himself. He had never been in love, despite numerous short-lived affairs. When in port, he could always find himself a willing woman, so why should he tie himself down for life? Yet that was exactly what he had intended from the moment he first saw her.

Yet, looking at her now, sensing the torment inside her, it was all he could do to keep from taking her in his arms, kissing those quivering lips, rousing her as he had that night. But he knew that if he did and she responded as she had then, she would not sleep alone tonight.

'Are you not curious as to our destination?' he mocked.

'It does not concern me.' She shrugged her shoulders briefly. If another port of call kept them away from his island a while longer, delayed the inevitable, then she was glad of it.

'I retain an excellent man of medicine on the island, and I told you Charity would be well cared for. Is there anything you need?'

'Nothing,' Angelina replied quickly, brushing aside the gesture. She wanted neither his kindness, nor his company. She wanted nothing from him.

'You will not best me like this, Angelina. You are hurting only yourself by being stubborn and foolish. Do not continue to fight me. We both know it is not what you want, and it is certainly not to my liking,' Raven said quietly. 'I know you fear me after what you have learnt.'

'I do not!' A chuckle rose in his throat at the swift denial.

'If it were otherwise, you would not be so nervous whenever I am near you,' he continued. 'Be honest with yourself—don't cheat yourself out of happiness.'

'You call this happiness?' Angelina cried, her temper rising. 'A prisoner on board your ship? I have little to look forward to when we reach this island of yours, have I?'

'Far more than you realise, if you admit your response when I rouse passion in you: you want more of my kisses, more of everything I offer!' Raven challenged, and she knew the colour was surging into her cheeks. 'If you spoke to me with your lips, angel, as the body does that betrays you when you are in my arms, then you might find not only happiness, but contentment, even fulfilment . . .'

No man had ever spoken to her thus in all her life, telling her what she should think and feel . . . but he was right, about everything. She hated him for it; that he was so experienced in such matters that he understood her feelings better than she did herself. Most of them frightened her. No well-brought-up young lady should feel as she did when a man held her.

'Accept it, angel,' Raven murmured, straightening. 'Accept your fate.'

Thinking he was going to seize hold of her and prove to her that she no longer had a will of her own where he was concerned, she backed away, the tears she had kept until control now streaming down over her cheeks. 'Never! Never!'

Picking up her skirts, she ran to the companion, almost knocking Raúl over as he appeared at the top of the stairs. Raven made no move to follow, knowing that nothing worth while could be achieved by upsetting her further. With a sigh he turned towards the quarterdeck, and the Spaniard fell in step beside him.

'I think you will have to beat that one, Capitán. She will not be easily tamed,' Raúl said with a one-sided grin.

'I don't want a broken doll, my friend. What I want is a woman.'

'Why that one?' Raven had never explained his reasons for bringing her on board, and Raúl knew better to ask, but his curiosity got the better of him at last. 'You could have any woman you pleased, without all this trouble. Even Jacquetta.'

'Jacquetta is your woman,' Raven replied somewhat drily. 'Angelina, for better or for worse, is mine. She has too much courage for her own good—too much damned independence! Did you see how she handled this ship?'

'I see the way she looks at you,' Raúl murmured. 'Sometimes with little doe eyes, all gentle, but mostly with daggers aimed at your back. That one is afraid of nothing. As I said, you should beat her!'

'I agree it might hasten a closer relationship, but I'll not lay a finger on her. To force a woman defiles the act of love. No, my friend, I shall continue to be patient.'

'You! ¡Dios mia! I think she has bewitched you. How can any man look at that one, and be patient?'

'I did not say I would be so—indefinitely.'

The days dragged with agonising slowness. The only relief for Angelina was her nightly sojourn on deck, but since that last occasion she was always careful to take it before Raven appeared; if that was not possible, she stayed at the far end, where she could ignore his presence. He never tried to make her join him. He was waiting for her to go to him, she thought. Let him wait—for ever!

When Stumpy told her they would be in sight of Raven's island home the following day around noon, she could have cried with delight. She tried to convey the welcome news to Charity, but received no indication that the woman understood.

That night Angelina was sure she would sleep soundly. Dry land at last! The long, lonely time at sea had been miserable and nerve-racking. She had hoped that the ship would call in at Jamaica, enabling her to spend a short while among civilised people again. She had made several good friends during her last trip there on the *White Swan*—and for a mad moment was struck with the idea of seeking help to escape from her present predicament. But that would mean leaving Charity behind, and she could not do that. But it was not to be. They did not stop at the island. Raven knew she had been to Jamaica before; that the thought of escape must cross her mind; and that she might try to reach it from his island. Yet he had not appeared in the least worried that she might try once again to flee from him.

How was it that he—a pirate—could drop anchor in Port Royal harbour and coolly go ashore without risk of being arrested and shipped back to England in irons? He was still a wanted fugitive as well as a pirate! She remembered the clothes in his closet; in those he would be accepted as a gentleman of means, and the aloofness of his arrogant manner would no doubt deter any questions.

She tossed and turned in the huge bed, trying desperately to snatch a few hours' rest before they arrived. When had she last had a full night's sleep? Then dreamed of London, and Edgar. She had returned in triumph from her last voyage and they had been celebrating the fixture of their wedding day. He was a little drunk, and coarser in his manner than she remembered, laughing at her pride in what she had achieved, as he poured himself more wine. When he attempted to pull her down onto the couch and make love to her, she pushed him away, revolted by his crude remarks.

He had grabbed her in his arms, pressing his lips on hers, and then, in her nightmare, his face changed. It was not Edgar who held her, but Raven . . . smothering her face with kisses that made her swoon with pure pleasure. She did not protest when *he* drew her down on to the couch beside him and caressed her until she lay acquiescent in his embrace.

And as she turned her face up to his, seeking his lips

with her own, pouring out her declaration of love, his features became cruel and mocking . . . He laughed at her admission, and told her that he had no interest in her other than as a weapon against his brother. The hands which held her fast were no longer gentle, but bit fiercely into her bare shoulders. The mouth which covered hers sought to crush with bitter, searing kisses, her resistance growing at his hateful words. She tried to fight him, but she had no strength against this monster that wanted her without one jot of honest feeling. She cried out in shame and despair.

She sprang up in bed to find that her nightgown was clinging to her perspiring body. Damp tendrils of loose hair stuck uncomfortably to her wet cheeks. As she smoothed them back from her face, she discovered that her hand was trembling. She would sleep no more tonight.

A sound from the direction of the door froze her where she sat. Moonlight flooded the bed, but beyond, the cabin was dark with shadows. There was someone there, standing in the doorway!

'Who—Who is it? Charity?' No! Not possible after the Madeira. She leapt from the bed, snatching up the silver candlestick from the table as she did so. Had one of Raven's crew grown more bold than the rest and decided to risk his captain's anger by invading her cabin in the dead of night? The door was closed when she reached it. She hesitated for a moment only before flinging it open and stepping out, candlestick upraised to deal a devastating blow to anyone hovering in the passage. It was empty. Not a sound . . . No movement.

Was she dreaming still, she wondered, as she went back inside and closed the door? There was no key to lock it. She discovered that it had been removed after her first attempted escape. Anyone could come and go as he pleased . . . Anyone foolish!

She had climbed back into bed and propped the pillows behind her head, determined not to close her eyes again for the rest of the night, when she saw them . . . her father's pair of pistols! Someone had placed them on the small table beside the bed. Raven had taken them from Charity and her the day he had attacked the *White Swan* . . . Why had he returned them? Of course they were not loaded, she thought, picking one up to examine it, and found to her astonishment—and further puzzlement—that it was. She had not been dreaming . . . He had come into her cabin and left them. Until the sky lightened and the rays of a weak sun invaded the cabin, she sat with the pistol clutched in her hand.

'When will we be going ashore?' She had dressed very early and waited for the sound of Raven's footsteps to tell her that he was returning to his cabin to rest. As he drew level with the door, she stepped out to confront him. She had not spoken to him for days, and was shocked at how tired he looked. Dark shadows deepened the colour of his eyes to the grey of storm clouds, and there was a growth of beard on his chin. She had never seen him unshaven before. Unlike most of the crew, who were heavily bearded or had moustaches or exceedingly unkempt hair, he was always well groomed. And was that the odour of rum she could smell about him?

Raven's expression was none too friendly as he regarded her. He was tired, and not in the best of tempers. It was the month for unpredictable hurricanes in the Caribbean, and the clouds massing in the sky told him he had been lucky to reach the island before a storm broke. He had spent the last two hours in Raúl's cabin, drinking with him. This had not improved his frame of mind, for all the other man could talk about was Angelina. His suggestions for bringing her to heel were many and varied. Raven no longer found the subject amusing.

'It has taken you longer than I anticipated to come round,' he remarked to her. 'But you have, which means you are concocting another little scheme or other in that nimble mind.'

'I am not!' she protested angrily. 'I want to go ashore, that's all. We have reached your island, haven't we? Why can't I? I want to see other people, just to walk . . . Please?'

She had never asked him for anything before. She had not meant to now, but the thought of remaining on board much longer was getting on her nerves. She had to *see* what was in store for her!

'I shall not try to escape. Where would I go?' she added.

'You told me that once before.' Silver flecks gleamed derisively in the grey depths.

'And I broke my word. I have never done so before. I am not proud of it,' she said, her lips beginning to tremble a little. She spun away when he did not reply; then, as she caught sight of the pistols on the bedside table, wheeled on him, demanding, 'Why did you come into my cabin last night?'

'I thought you might feel safer with the protection I left for you. They are loaded, as you have probably found out for yourself by now.'

'Why? Are you so sure of yourself that you do not think I would shoot you in self-defence?' He was playing some game with her, she decided, but she could not see how he would profit from it. 'If I dared use them against you, I know exactly what my fate would be at the hands of your crew,' she declared. 'I am sure you know I will do nothing against you while Charity is so ill and in need of care.'

Raven fixed her with a piercing gaze that seemed to penetrate to her very soul. For a moment she sensed that he was reluctant to speak what was in his mind.

'My ward, Drusilla, was a very lovely child. Would the man who savagely attacked her and brought about her death be so foolhardy as to place himself at such a disadvantage? Think about it until we go ashore.'

Was he intimating that he had *not* killed her? Angelina raised a hand to her forehead, her mind reeling. Then, as he moved past her, she realised what he had said.

'When? Soon?' She could not hide the pleasure from her voice; she was too overcome with relief even to try.

'After the ship has been unloaded. Please stay in your cabin until I come for you. I don't want you wandering about on deck.' But why? her eyes questioned, even before the words came to her lips. 'That is an order, Angelina. While the cargo is being discharged, keep to yourself. I don't want you in the way. Stay in your cabin.'

'Very well.'

As it grew lighter and a sweltering sun beat down upon the upper desk, the temperature in the cabin rose quickly, and she opened the windows to allow in what little breeze there was. The banging and pounding coming from above was making her head ache, but she dared not set foot outside the door, knowing that to risk Raven's anger now would mean the certain curtailment of any privileges he might allow her in the future.

CHAPTER
EIGHT

RAVEN CAME for her late that afternoon. Angelina had been pacing the floor for hours, listening to the laughter and merrymaking which still continued on the deck above. The crew were drinking, now that the holds had been cleared, and by the noise they were making, dividing up the booty from their long months at sea. Two longboats had gone to the shore and returned countless times, carrying men and sacks, sea-chests and livestock. Pigs squealed and struggled as they were lowered in nets to the waiting boats. One got away, wriggling out of the mass of seething bodies, and fell into the sea. A pirate dived overboard to rescue it, and succeeded in dragging two of his companions into the water with him in their frantic attempts to hoist the animal to safety.

The sight of their funny antics had brought a smile to her lips, but that had been hours ago, and the moment of amusement gone, her thoughts turned again to the island and the house where she was expected to spend the rest of her days as Raven's mistress.

Her eyes lingered on the sandy beach which stretched for miles in either direction. Tall palms bent beneath the increasing wind, which was sending black clouds racing across the sky. They were in for bad weather—and soon, she realised. A heavy swell was growing, and the movements of the ship as it rode at anchor were noticeably more violent. White-crested waves pounded the sand, where the provisions were hastily being hoisted on to the backs of the crew and hurried to safety. The *Sea Witch* was anchored in a sheltered lagoon on the far side of coral reefs, the sight of which had made Angelina's heart leap into her mouth many times as Raven negotiated the narrow passage through them to the tranquil water beyond. Although she might be pounded by fierce waves, she was in the protective encirclement of towering sandstone cliffs on three sides, safe from the ocean which was now beginning to seethe and bubble like a cauldron.

'Are you ready?' As Raven's voice sounded behind her, Angelina turned from the window. He had a wide-brimmed hat pulled well down over his face, and a long black cloak covered him completely. She saw he carried another of blue velvet, which he held out to her. 'The storm is almost upon us. If we do not hurry, we shall not reach the house before the rains come; so make up your mind whether you are coming or not.'

What did he expect her to do? she thought, with a spark of anger showing in her eyes as she went to him and allowed him to place the velvet about her. Stay on board and ride out the storm? Alone? His fingers lingered for a moment longer than was necessary on her bare skin as he fastened the silver clasp, his eyes searching her face. She refused to look at him, keeping her own fixed rigidly on the opposite wall.

'Charity . . .' she began as he drew her into the passage.

'Already ashore. We are the last to leave.'

The strength of the wind was unbelievable. Angelina was almost blown off her feet as she stepped out on the deck. Her cloak billowed about her like a sail. The cowl was torn from her head, and her loose hair whipped in wild profusion around her face, blinding her until she again managed to secure it.

She was grateful for the arm Raven slipped about her shoulders to steady her, though she would never have admitted it to him. Several times she was forced to clutch at him to keep her balance as he helped her to the longboat, but once safely in it, she drew as far away from him as possible, hugging her cloak about her, her face averted once more.

Brief though the crossing was, she was glad to be lifted out on to the sand. The pitching of the boat as it rose and fell, negotiating the enormous waves, often sent her sprawling against the hardness of Raven's body time and time again. He was like a rock, unyielding against the force of the wind and the rain that now lashed at them mercilessly, soaking them to the skin. He seemed concerned neither for the fury of the elements or for the icy spray which constantly broke over them.

Angelina had heard tales of the havoc these storms could cause, the destruction left in their wake. Houses blown away, crops ruined, ships sunk beneath waves of enormous magnitude. This was her first experience of being caught in one, and she sincerely hoped her last. She was terrified by the howling wind and the force with which it buffeted her.

The heels of her shoes sank deep into the wet sand as she struggled to make headway in the face of the gale. It took all her strength to pull them free—it felt like quicksand trying to imprison her until the ocean came close enough to claim her—and limped on, leaving one behind.

The palms fringing the beach swayed and bent until she thought they would snap in half. There was not one patch of clear sky to be seen, only thunderous black clouds racing above their heads, like the devil riding a whirlwind, with his pack of snarling, baying hounds in full pursuit. Or was the devil being welcomed back to his island domain, she wondered, snatching a quick look into Raven's face close by hers as he helped her along. Had she not known otherwise, she would have thought the time closer to nine at night than five in the afternoon, so dark had it become. The island, which had looked pleasant and welcoming when she surveyed it from the ship, now appeared evil and menacing to her, waiting to enfold her in its embrace—an embrace from which she would never escape if her companion had his way. And she could no longer see any avenues open to her. She was alone and friendless . . . trapped here for ever.

Stumbling, she fell to her knees, her cloak gaping open as she lost her grip on it. She gasped as rain battered her bare skin, soaking through the beautiful yellow silk gown she wore, running in streams inside her bodice, chilling her to the bone.

Raven bent and gathered her into his arms, carrying her with effortless ease the last few yards over the beach and into the undergrowth of dense trees, which afforded them some, if not very much, shelter from the onslaught beyond, shouldering his way through philodendron and wild oleander, heavy with flowers even at this late time in the year. In England the flowers would be dying, she found herself thinking. Everyone would be awaiting the arrival of winter, cold and frost, snow. Angelina pressed her face into the comfort of Raven's shoulder as he followed in the wake of his men, oblivious of the wet cloth against her cheek which was as saturated as her own clothes. Held so close to him, the storm held no fears for her.

They were climbing a steep hill, she realised, as she heard the breath rasping in his throat and his heart pounding with exertion, although he did not slow his fast pace. At least she had established that he did have a heart—she had begun to wonder, after his treatment of her these past weeks! How strong he was, carrying her as if she weighed nothing at all. Many of the men ahead were stumbling under the weight of their burdens, for the sacks they carried shoulder high were sodden with water, and doubtless twice as heavy. Muffled curses were carried away on the wind.

What was wrong with her that she was afraid of his arms about her; not proud or indeed flattered by his determined efforts not only to have her—but to keep her! Other women would not have been so particular. Had they met in London or elsewhere under different circumstances, and he had gone to the same trouble in wooing her, Angelina knew she would have been swept off her feet, and revelling in the fact. Was he not handsome, the most handsome man she had ever known? And rich, owning not only his own ship, but a whole island? His wealth must surely compare with that of the dukes and earls she had brushed shoulders with at the court of the King.

He was a man of the world, which she found oddly reassuring when she recollected the gawky, inexperienced boys who had sought to court her, seeking to find their manhood in her bed. He had led her confidently and unhurriedly into a gradual awakening and awareness of her own sensuality, which in itself she found a little alarming, for she had never considered herself either passionate or seductive. Now that he was home again, his authority unchallenged in this place, would he take what he wanted from her and satisfy his own desires, leaving hers unrequited? Was that why he had been so casual in his handling of her, showing her his mastery one moment; the next, leaving her alone to brood? He had all the time in the world!

If only he were not a pirate! Yet even *that* she could accept and put to the back of her mind as she lay in his arms and thrilled to his kisses, for her love was strong enough, deep enough, to overcome her natural revulsion for his unsavoury way of life. But while the stigma of murder hung over his head . . . Surely he would not keep her here with him, now that she knew the truth? To share the bed and endure the touch of a man who had raped his own ward in a jealous fit of temper . . . She would die!

A long tremor ran through her body. Thinking the cold was growing too much for her, Raven clutched her more tightly against his chest.

'Nearly there.' She barely heard the words, even though his mouth was close against her ear.

Angelina raised her head, curious to see the house that he intended should be her home from now on. Rain stung her eyes, making it almost impossible to pick out anything clearly, but she did glimpse several outbuildings off to one side. Most of the men with the provisions seemed to be heading in that direction. Raven had turned away, along a narrow pathway where flowering bushes brushed against his cloak as he passed. It was a kind of garden, she imagined, starved of a woman's love to bring it to life. Flowers were overgrown with weeds, flowering cacti overshadowed delicate orchids. It was easy to think of herself as one of those pale pink orchids being threatened by Raven, the prickly cactus with his needle-like thorns.

Ahead of them lay a sprawling house of indefinable length at least two storeys high. Steps, which Raven took two at a time without slowing his pace, led up to a sheltered veranda where bougainvillaeas and bright red flamboyants, their wide petals heavy with glistening raindrops, twined thickly in and out of the many white-washed arches.

He kicked open an enormous door with a booted foot, and yelled out a name at the top of his voice as he set Angelina down. He booted it closed with obvious relief. Silence! The walls must have been at least four or five feet thick to shut out the noise so effectively, she real-ised, gazing round her and trying hard to keep the incredulity from her face as she saw the kind of place he had brought her to.

She had not known what to expect. Comfort—Yes, Raven liked his comfort and good food and fine clothes; she had learned that much about him. But this house . . .

They stood in a low-beamed room with a stone floor. The walls were brilliantly white and rather bare, but she came to the conclusion that this was only an entrance hall as a man came running forward to take Raven's dripping cloak. She was so engrossed in her surround-ings that Raven had unfastened the blue velvet and lifted it from her before she became aware of what he was doing. He gave a soft exclamation at the sight of the sodden yellow gown, and Angelina, as she looked down at it too, became acutely conscious of how it was clinging to the curves of her figure, outlining the roundness of her breasts, the smallness of her waist, the lithe curve of hips and thighs, as though she had nothing on at all!

'Matty has prepared the rooms? Hot water?' Raven demanded of the servant. He was an enormous man, with muscles such as she had never seen before on long, coal-black arms. A Negro! So Raven owned slaves also! Soon she would be joining their ranks until he tired of her. For a moment she was reminded of Sharlock, for both men were about the same height and build, but this one had kind eyes . . . rather gentle, brown eyes which reminded her of one of the doleful spaniels King Charles always carried with him.

As if sensing her thought, Raven said smilingly, 'This is Caleb. He runs the house with his wife, Matty, who, as you will discover, is the best cook you will ever meet. She is a veritable jewel among women, able to turn her hand to anything at all. She will fuss over you like a mother hen, give you a hefty shoulder to weep on, should the mood ever take you . . . and, if I don't get you upstairs and into a hot tub within the next few minutes, will accuse me of trying to cause you to go down with a chill.'

To the Negro, he said, 'The other woman is comfortable? She has everything she needs?' He brushed raindrops from his hair.

'Matty gave her some of her herb tea the moment she arrived, Captain. She's resting now . . . asleep, I wouldn't wonder. She looked exhausted,' the man returned, and revealed brilliant white teeth as he smiled.

'She was, poor thing.' Taking Angelina's hand, Raven led her up a flight of wide stone steps inlaid with green and black marble to the upper floor. She went willingly, wanting only to submerge herself in hot, scented water —if such a luxury was possible amid the barbarity of a pirate's lair—and to relax and allow her tensions and fears to be soothed away. When she had done that, she would emerge in full control of herself again, ready to do battle for her honour. 'Poor Angelina, too,' Raven added, as he ushered her into one of the rooms off a long corridor, where the windows were heavily shuttered against the weather. Candles flickered in wrought-iron

holders high on the walls to light their way. She glimpsed
paintings in golden frames, tapestries, and vases filled
with sweet-smelling flowers before she entered the room
he had chosen for her.

The walls were hung with burgundy silk. Matching
curtains hung round the huge four-poster bed against the
far wall. The curtains at the windows were burgundy
velvet, with gold embroidery. The furniture was heavy,
oak mostly—but had been inlaid with gold leaf in the
most intricate designs. There was a walnut chest of
drawers, a couch beneath the window covered in gold
velvet with minute hanging tassels. At the end of the
bed a sea-chest, again carved and inlaid, this time with
ivory workmanship, of which the delicacy struck her
speechless. She had never imagined anything like
this!

'There is an adjoining sitting-room,' Raven told her,
'but you can see that later. Off with that dress now
before you catch your death of cold. I don't want you to
become ill at this stage,' he added with a wicked grin,
which brought the colour surging into her pale cheeks.
He was different—more casual, horribly more confident
—she thought as her fingers reached automatically for
the fastening of her bodice. Then they fell away and he
swore as she stared at him defiantly.

'This is no time for modesty, angel. Do as I say, damn
you, quickly. You are shivering, girl.'

'What am I supposed to do—wrap myself in the
bedsheets?' she flung back. 'My clothes were left on
board the *Sea Witch*.'

'You shall have them tomorrow,' he chuckled. Flinging open a door, he pulled out a velvet robe trimmed
with fur. Sable, Angelina saw as he tossed it to her. She
found that the wardrobe was crammed full of dresses of

every description . . . and shelves lined with shoes . . . and dainty leather boots with coloured heels. 'Where is that woman?'

He strode to the door, opened it wide, and bellowed, 'Matty! My guest is dying of cold. Where is that tub? And water? Are you all asleep down there?'

While his back was towards her, Angelina tore off her clothes in frantic haste and was belting the robe about her when he turned. She was unaware of how it clung to her slender curves as seductively as the wet gown. Raven saw it, however, and a smile touched his lips. He swept a hand in the direction of the dressing-table beside another window. 'You'll find everything you need there. Slippers are in the closet. Ask Matty if you require anything that is not here. I'm going to change, too. I'll bring something to warm us in a moment.'

Angelina's mouth grew dry as he turned on his heel and disappeared through a door off to her left; not the one through which they had entered. Were her rooms connected to his? How convenient! She had no time to give more than a cursory inspection to the things lying on the dressing-table: sweet-smelling ointments in pretty glass containers, a silver-backed comb and brush and a hand mirror were in plain view on the silk-covered top. Beneath the lavish frills were probably drawers, for she had one very similar at home; but what they contained, she did not try to imagine.

The woman who appeared in the doorway was so large that it was an effort for her to get through the opening even by turning sideways. She was followed by the figure of Caleb, carrying a gold and white porcelain tub which also had trouble making an entry. At last successfully in the room, it was set down at the far end on a rush mat, beside a chair where Angelina saw that towels and soap had already been laid out. She had no complaints about her treatment so far.

'Well now, ain't you a drowned chicken! Whatever was that man thinking of letting you get all wet like this—shame on him! Ole Matty will have his hide if you go down with a chill, don't you fret about that. Men!'

The woman surveyed Angelina, her hands thrust down upon ample hips. As a shiver ran through the robed form, she turned on the silent Negro behind her, demanding, 'And what are you standing there for? Where's my hot water? The child will be in need of a doctor if you don't stir yourself. Run, man—use those fine legs the Almighty gave you . . . plenty of it, mind.'

Angelina's face broke into a smile as Caleb scuttled from the room without a word. So huge a man, but gentle, as she had suspected when she first saw him. No doubt he had often been on the wrong end of his wife's sharp tongue—perhaps more. Matty looked as if she could wield a hefty broom with great success.

'Men!' Matty grumbled again, shaking her head from side to side in vexation. 'Never have found a one capable of thinking for himself.'

'Am I being maligned again?' Raven came into the room, having discarded his wet clothes, and he was wearing dry breeches which looked as if they had been tailored from the hide of some animal. A spotless white shirt hung open across his chest. In his hands he held a glass decanter and two glasses. 'What am I in trouble for, now?'

'Lettin' this poor child get the soakin' of her life. I shouldn't wonder if she doesn't go down with a fever by morning.'

'Then feed her some of your special herb tea, and see she does not,' Raven chuckled. 'If you were to dry her hair somewhat it might help matters,' he added, eyeing Angelina's dripping tresses. Muttering under her breath, Matty fetched a large white towel from the linen cupboard, sat her down in a velvet-covered chair, and began to rub it dry. 'And this will keep you warm until the hot water arrives.'

'I don't like it,' Angelina said, staring at the dark liquid in the glass he was holding out to her. She remembered only too clearly how it had warmed and relaxed her that night in Tortuga . . . the night she had almost surrendered to him! Was it his intention to mellow her again tonight so that she would not object to his advances?

'Nevertheless you will drink it. Good girl.' He watched half of it disappear down her throat. 'All of it, and then I shall show you the rest of you rooms. By the look of it, it will be morning before the water arrives.'

The glance he shot at Matty sent her waddling at a fast pace to the open door. Her powerful lungs exploded into a tirade that could probably be heard in every room in the house, Angelina thought, trying hard not to smile.

Satisfied that every drop of rum had been drained from the glass, Raven stood back, indicating that she should follow him. She wanted to pretend she did not care what the rest of the rooms were like, but the sight of the wardrobe full of clothes had roused her curiosity.

'I see you are accustomed to entertaining often,' she said cuttingly, casting a meaningful glance in the direction of its bulging interior. 'Clothes provided to fit all occasions. Do you not have a little trouble fitting your guests, even from that varied assortment?'

Raven's amused eyes met and held hers for a moment before he surveyed the contents of the wardrobe. She saw he could hardly contain his mirth at her remarks, which had been intended to make him feel uncomfortable, at least—certainly not amused. Had he no shame? Behind Angelina, Matty gave a giggle of pure mirth as she again went to the door to listen for Caleb's return.

'Bless the child, have you not told her the saintly life you lead here, Captain? Never has he brought a lady of quality here—nor one of any other kind, though I dare say he's had his fair share of them away from here. My man Caleb thinks you must be something really special for him to go to all the trouble of . . .'

'Matty!' The glare Raven directed towards her froze her into silence. 'You clucking hen! I suppose the whole island knows by now . . . Women, dammit! Can't keep their tongues still or a secret safe. Though I'm grateful for the praising of my non-existent virtues, Matty, I am quite capable of speaking for myself. Not that it is necessary. Miss Blackthorne is rapidly becoming well aware of my resourcefulness—and determination. This is your sitting-room.'

He showed Angelina into a large room as comfortably furnished as the bedroom. Here the main colours were varying shades of yellow. From the brightness of spring primroses to the deep honeyed tones of amber. There were shuttered doors which led out to a balcony, he told her as her eyes surveyed it in admiration. An artist's eye had decorated and furnished the room. The furniture was small, almost dainty: a sofa and two matching chairs in walnut, covered with yellow velvet; several matching footstools; a rosewood escritoire; a day-bed with soft cushions beneath a smaller window.

'Do you find your accommodation satisfactory?' Raven enquired.

How she wished he had not presented her with such elaborate surroundings, such comfort. She was greatly reminded of her bedroom at home, also furnished in rich burgundy, her favourite colour. What a coincidence that he had chosen it. Coincidence? Her heart somersaulted unsteadily. Was anything coincidental where Raven was concerned?

He was watching her with narrowed gaze, a smouldering look in those grey eyes which stirred excitement within her, and made her remember his burning kisses, his bold caresses. The smile at the corners of his mouth grew with her silence.

'I have achieved a small miracle. A woman lost for words,' he mocked. He allowed his gaze to wander past the damp hair lying about her shoulders, to the seductive curves outlined against the velvet robe.

Inwardly choking with indignation at the way he was deliberately undressing her, she found her voice at last.

'My rooms are—very pleasant,' she admitted. She knew she should have spoken out against them, found fault in some way, but she could not—for there was none to find. They were fit for royalty! Yet, despite the begrudging admiration which brought sudden warmth to his expression, something she rarely saw, she added, 'No doubt your other guests also found them adequate.'

'No one but you has seen them. No one but you will use them. I did not have them furnished in this manner, with personal items such as only you are accustomed to, to provide enjoyment for any other woman. Matty told you the truth—you are the first I have brought beneath this roof since I came to live here. Do you not see how patient I have been all this time, waiting for the perfection I knew I should one day find to grace my home?' He was laughing at her, she decided, yet his eyes were serious indeed, the smile on his face slightly whimsical—hopeful, perhaps, that she would believe his fairy-tale?

'Do you think me weak in the head to believe such a lie?' she challenged.

'You are a young woman of great strength of character and a determination which, I must admit, has roused me to great anger at times. You have a stubborn trait, too, but I forgive you that, for I suffer from the same affliction.' Raven's eyes had gleamed at the angry note in her tone. How well she hid her astonishment, but he knew that she would soon have to accept the truth of what he said. It was only the first of many surprises—all of which he considered most pleasant—that she was about to receive. For an instant he considered confiding his plans—his dreams—to her in the hope that the barrier of fear and mistrust between them would be swept away.

He decided reluctantly that the time was not yet. Too much at this time might have the reverse affect and drive her further away from him. In a few days—when she had come to accept that this was her home, and that she would know no other; and that she and she alone was mistress here, in total control of all that involved—then he would be free with his words.

'But why all this?'

Angelina's fingers clutched nervously at her robe. She had never believed him when he insisted so fervently on his desire to have her, and on the money and time he had spent to discover her every movement, the most intimate details of her life and background. But was not the proof now before her eyes? Was there nothing he did not know about her life? No wonder the bedroom was furnished as it was; it would have been a small detail, among everything else he sought to know, to find out her deep passion for the colour burgundy.

'Why not?' he countered. 'Did I not say I would give you the best of everything? This is but a small part of what you will have, my angel. I want you to be happy here with me. Do you not agree that my efforts have been worth while? The wardrobe I have provided is suitable for any occasion—here, or at court in England. Lady Castlemaine would be speechless with jealousy to find you alongside her.'

He had chosen that, too! The colour fled from Angelina's cheeks, returning to redden them with fierce embarrassment as she realised the implications. He knew her every measurement—no wonder the robe she wore fitted her so snugly! A trifle too snugly for her liking, she thought, aware of his gaze resting on the creamy fullness of her breast above the curving neckline. Did he expect her to dress to please him?

More frustrating still was her discovery that, not even among the wardrobe she had left behind her, which contained the latest fashions from France and the newest materials, there was not a gown to compare with those she had briefly glimpsed! They had been chosen with the same experienced eye and good taste that had produced such a masterpiece in these two rooms he had given her.

From the bedroom came the sound of water being splashed into the tub, and Matty's authoritative tones ordering more—and still more—and hot, so that her charge would not freeze to death while she soaked.

Angelina found herself growing quite lightheaded at the prospect he dangled before her, like a juicy carrot before a starving donkey: mistress of this fine house; mistress of a handsome man of great wealth; a chance to enjoy his kisses once again, the touch of his hands which roused the woman in he so successfully. He would never know how she thrilled to these things, believing instead that her submission had been prompted by an acceptance of her fate.

What did it matter if she was mistress, not wife? She loved him. It would be better than living her life without him, forced to seek second best in the arms of another who would never incite her to passion as he had, tortured by memories she could not forget—or admit to anyone. But even as she wavered, seeking the words to somehow tell him of her feelings, the past rose up to dull the brightness of the future he proposed for her.

'You expect a great deal from me; more than I am willing to give. Find yourself another woman eager to be in my place. I am sure there must be one . . . more than one.' Her voice was shrill with emotion.

Raven could almost feel the fear radiating from her. What had brought it about? For a moment he had felt he was overcoming the high wall separating them, as he had on the night in Tortuga. 'As you say, more than one, perhaps—but this is for you and no one else,' he told her grave-faced. His sincerity could not be doubted.

'When you discovered I was betrothed to your brother, did that intensify your—desire—to have me?' Angelina cried, stepping back from him. Attack, attack! her heart cried. Do not let him sense how vulnerable you are. One touch—one kiss—and she knew she would be lost for ever in the fires of hell which would surely claim her for her surrender to this devil!

'I admit, if I so choose, that it would give me another weapon against him. Not that I am in need of one. I have deprived him of his ships, and often of his men—and now I have taken his bride from him.' Raven fixed her with an odd look—a mixture of sadness and anger flickering in the silver depths of his eyes, as if he were fighting an inward battle with them both. What reason had he to fight either, since he had everything he wanted, she thought, turning back towards the bedroom with a sense of relief as Matty called out her name.

'And you deprive me of my freedom and bring me to this prison,' she retorted bitterly.

The Negress caught the words, and threw a startled look at the man behind her. A slight shake of the head warned her to remain silent or incur his wrath.

'It need not be,' Raven assured her as he followed. 'You should feel flattered to have a man so enamoured of you.'

'It is no compliment. Your fine words are wasted on me. I know the true reason you abducted me—to spite Edgar!' She wheeled on him, eyes blazing like magnificent emeralds, her young face set with indignation. 'It is little wonder he hates you. You have taken everything from him. If it suits you, you will use me against him, I know it!'

'It was a passing thought, no more. Don't fight me, angel.'

Her lips pressed tightly together at the use of the hateful name. An angel of destruction—yes, she would be that! To strike him down, render him as helpless as he wished her to be. At her mercy, not his! Did she really want him in such a way? Broken, at the end of a noose on Hangman's Wharf? No, no, not that! She wanted her freedom, but she did not wish for his death. He would return from the grave to haunt her, invading her dreams and her thoughts until he drove her quite mad with longing for him.

'What would await you in England, should you return? What have you to go back to that is so inviting? A man who would marry you solely for enough money to extricate himself from a very perilous position with his creditors. At least I have been honest with you. You cannot deny that.'

'I was to have *married* Edgar. I would have been his wife, not his mistress,' she flung back, her cheeks flushing again. 'I would not marry *you* if you gave me a chest full of treasure.'

'What about two?' Raven chuckled.

'I cannot be bought!'

'But you have been, my sweet, with the lives of the crew of the *White Swan*,' he reminded her with a cruel twist to his lips, and she flinched as if he had struck her. 'Your promise—for what it is worth and we shall soon discover that—gave them their freedom.'

'Freedom?' she echoed, not understanding. 'You said they had remained behind in Tortuga.'

'They sailed for England as soon as their cargo had been unloaded. I gave Captain Forrester a little message for my brother to the effect that he can come and get you if he still wants you. He won't, of course.'

'I hate you!' Angelina spat the words at him, appalled by the deception. 'You let me believe they were still hostages for my—my good behaviour.'

'I see no reason to hold their fate as a threat over your head. It never was, if you remember. You offered to make such a bargain,' he murmured with a shrug. She could scarcely restrain her desire to slap him.

'But you gave me to understand . . .' Her voice trailed off in horror. Now she thought carefully about it, as he had reminded her before, she had made the first move. She had placed herself—albeit unwittingly—in his hands.

She was aware of a broad smile spreading across Matty's face as Raven took her in his arms, a hand curving into the small of her back to press her body boldly against his. She blushed at the intimate embrace before a servant—not that the woman acted as such at all, despite her colour—and threw back her head to challenge his right to subject her to such an indignity . . . but the words were never uttered.

Silver flints glinted and sparked in the grey caverns of Raven's eyes as he lowered his mouth to hers. With an expertise that weakened her knees and made her forget every resolve to resist him, he parted her quivering lips, plying them with searing kisses that unleashed the wild passion that she knew could destroy her. Her fingers clutched at the fabric of his shirt as she pressed herself more tightly against the broad chest, thrilling to the hardness of his thighs, seeking more—and more. She never wanted him to stop!

She heard Raven's sharp intake of breath as her fingers crept upwards to entwine themselves in his thick black hair. She was answering him kiss for kiss, with a hunger in them to match his own. She was his! She might try to deny it, but her body declared it, betraying every word she had said to be a lie. His for the taking! The exultation which swept through him bore him along like a tidal wave, lifting him to a hitherto unknown lofty peak, and he rode it with his heart soaring with joy. Never had any woman moved him so!

Matty's voice from behind washed him up on to the dry sand of a deserted beach, after she had emitted a familiar grunt of disapproval.

'I suppose I'll get the blame when that girl has to soak herself in cold water. The trouble I had gettin' it up here, too, with that lazy, no-good Caleb draggin' his heels . . . as if he had all the time in the world.'

Angelina knew that it was with great reluctance that

Raven released her. And even greater reluctance on her part as she drew back from him. In those few brief, but spell-binding moments she had become so sure of what she wanted—and of the price she must pay to get it.

'I think it would be best if Matty brought you something to eat up here, and then you have an early night . . . If the storm will allow any of us any sleep,' he said. The howl of the gale could clearly be heard in the room now, despite the thickness of the walls and the heavily shuttered windows. She looked apprehensively towards the windows, where the rain was beating fiercely against the outside shutters. 'Don't worry, this old place will not be badly damaged. The barns may suffer, being constructed only of wood, but we can rebuild those. It's the villagers I am concerned for.'

'Villagers? Your men?'

'And their families—wives and sweethearts. A few traders who set up store when they found they could get a fair deal here for their goods. The Spanish Don who lived here before me did not allow the people to work for themselves, only for him and the greater good of his self-esteem. I permit free trade with whatever ships care to call here, so long as no one is cheated. We have a thriving community in the valley beyond; even a minister, who took up residence here two months ago, seeking to convert our ungodly souls. And a church—of sorts. It is little more than a shack at present; but, who knows, one day we might build a proper one.'

Had he not sounded so sincere, Angelina would have found the idea of bloodthirsty pirates settling down within the framework of wedded bliss a ludicrous prospect. But they were men, after all, she admitted to herself, and some might welcome the comfort and security a wife and children could give them. It might even induce them to give up their loathsome way of life—and that could not be a bad thing.

Raven leaned forward and kissed her lightly on the lips.

'I'll take my leave of you. No more disturbances tonight. When we meet again tomorrow, my angel, let us be as we are now.' He swung about on the Negress silently watching them, and gave her a hearty slap across her wide rear as he moved past her to the door. 'Take good care of her, or I'll have your hide, woman,' he warned.

'Get you gone then, and let me be about my business,' Matty said, shooing him outside and chosing the door. With a heavy sigh, she came to Angelina and helped her out of her robe. For a moment the liquid brown eyes surveyed intently, but not rudely, the milk-white skin, the soft rounded curves and long legs. 'Smitten he is, and it's no wonder, looking at what you have to offer him. Into the tub with you, little mistress.'

'Tell me about this island, Matty . . .' Angelina sank beneath the water, scented with heady oils. She hoped the woman would fill in all the gaps that Raven had left void. How had he come here? How could he live here like a king, with the island of Jamaica, which was under British rule and therefore a potential danger to him, so close at hand? Were the authorities unaware of his true identity? How were his visits there unchallenged? 'And the house . . . I want to know everything.'

'Child, it would take a month of Sundays to tell you everything.' Matty took a large sponge and a thin wedge of soap and began to lather her shoulders and back. Angelina gave herself into the capable hands ministering to her, feeling the tension ebb from her tired limbs. Even the sound of the storm outside did not bother her. Raven had deliberately left her to spend the rest of the evening alone. Had he suspected how shaken she was? Was he being kind and thoughtful, intending to give her ample time to compose herself? She had not expected him to consider her feelings at all, now that she was in his domain—and at his mercy. Such unexpected humanity had greatly lessened her fear of her inevitable surrender . . . and left her more confused than before in her assessment of the man.

CHAPTER
NINE

ANGELINA AWOKE the following morning to find the bed, and indeed the whole room, bathed in bright sunshine. She could not believe the swift change in the weather, and sleepily crawled from her warm, comfortable haven to go to the windows. The sky was clear and blue. Sea-birds swooped low over the brilliant silver sands, searching for food, their cries piercing the stillness of the morning. It was very quiet, she realised. Not a breath of wind to stir the tall palms which yesterday had been bowing to less than half their normal height in the face of the oncoming hurricane.

Where the sea merged with the sky it was blue, but nearer the beach it was a translucent green, shimmering in the sunlight. A great deal of driftwood had been washed ashore, she saw, and her eyes flew to the cove where the *Sea Witch* was moored. She rode at anchor, her sails furled. There were men on board; she could just make out tiny figures moving on deck. Perhaps it had not escaped totally unscathed.

From the window she had not only a perfect view of the beach and the dense wooded area through which Raven had carried her, but much more. Following the curve of the beach, she beheld tall mountains shrouded in mist, the base of them surrounded by a blanket of greenery. In the other direction were acres and acres of maize and sweet potatoes, but they had not escaped the storm, and most lay flattened and sodden, steaming in the heat of the day. So the island was productive in some ways and not just a haven for pirates, she mused, turning away as there came a knock on the door.

A woman not much older than Angelina came in, carrying a tray. She was slender and very dark, with more than a hint of both Spanish and African blood in her. She wore a brightly coloured skirt, which swirled around trim ankles as she advanced into the room and put the tray down on a small table. Long black hair streamed past brown shoulders, bared provocatively by the lowness of the white blouse she wore. The eyes which considered Angelina were as black as night—and very unfriendly.

'Matty say bring breakfast to Raven's woman. I bring,' she said in stilted English. 'But I am not your slave.'

'No, of course not,' Angelina said quickly. She was going to need all the friends she could accumulate on the island, but somehow she sensed that this girl resented her presence. 'What is your name?'

'Jacquetta.' She smiled craftily, considering the slim figure garbed in a diaphanous nightgown that left little to the imagination, for it was almost transparent. A froth of white lace hid the fullness of Angelina's breasts, and was as far as the nightgown went for providing decent cover. She had looked at it in horror when Matty had shown it to her, and demanded another . . . only to discover that all those in the drawer were equally seductive. Raven expected her to wear them in his presence! How those grey eyes would gleam and grow bolder when they glimpsed what awaited him. 'I, too, am Raven's woman. Your coming will change nothing.'

Angelina blenched at the words. Of course he had had other women, she never imagined otherwise. But to bring her beneath the same roof where his mistress resided!

'I shall not fight you for him.' Somehow she managed to give a careless shrug of her shoulders and sat down on the edge of the bed, crossing long legs. The silk slipped away from slender calf and neat ankles, and she saw Jacquetta frown as she realised the extent of the competition. 'You can have him, for all I care! If I could find someone to help me to leave this wretched island, I would be gone tomorrow.'

The girl had obviously come to taunt her with being second best in Raven's affections, Angelina thought, as she gave a toss of her loose hair and slammed out of the room.

How dare he humiliate her so! And after all his fine words, too. 'When we meet again tomorrow, let us be as we are now,' he had said, and she, in her stupidity, had been ready and willing to accept her fate. Now, if he walked through the door at that moment, Angelina thought she would cheerfully kill him. She loved him. Her body cried out to be satiated in his arms . . . Damn him! She would fight him tooth and nail before she gave in to him now. Let him go to Jacquetta, with whom he had probably spent the night. No wonder he had not been over-anxious to remain with her; he had a substitute!

She had lost her appetite for the hot chocolate provided in a tall porcelain pot and the plate of eggs and maize cakes. Returning to the window, she stared out across the bay to the *Sea Witch*. She was not a difficult ship to manage. With less than a dozen men to handle her, she could sail her back to England. But would she find such men on Raven's island, who were willing to betray their captain and abandon their way of life here?

When not at sea, she imagined that their existence would be very comfortable. He had sounded so sincere when he spoke of his concern for 'his' villagers. The wretch! He had deliberately played on her sympathy and succeeded in arousing compassion in her. Never again! She would not believe a word he said!

Below, off to the right of the house as she stood, were the out-buildings she had briefly seen in the rain. A young boy was leading out two horses. The coat of one gleamed and shone like a raven's wing in the sunlight. Instinctively she knew whom he belonged to, and her suspicion was confirmed as Raven came into view. And clinging to his arm, gazing up into the sunburnt features with adoration written all over her face, was Jacquetta.

Angelina pressed a hand to her heart and felt it begin to throb madly. The sight of him with another woman aroused such jealousy in her that she was deeply shaken and ashamed. Why did she have to love such a man? Jacquetta was obviously the kind of woman he preferred, easy-going, accessible . . . He would not have to use devious methods to get her into his bed.

She heard Jacquetta's laughter as he lifted her into the saddle of the waiting roan mare. She was still holding his arm, and then she bent her dark head and kissed him! Angelina thrust her hands over her eyes to shut out the dreaded sight of the two of them together. When she looked again, they were riding at a fast pace towards the forest on the far side of the house.

'Why, child, you've not eaten a thing!' Matty stood looking with a puzzled frown at the untouched tray. 'I admit I'm more used to feeding only a man in the house, but you look to me as if you could do with a little fat on those bones. No offence meant, mind, but my man says a woman should always look a woman.'

'Then I suggest you give the extra food to Jacquetta,' Angelina declared icily. 'I shall not eat one morsel while I am beneath this roof. I will starve to death first.'

'Don't imagine for one moment the captain would let you do that,' the woman answered, lifting her shoulders in exasperation. 'And why should I give good food to that fancy madam, when she has a husband to provide for her? Tell me that.'

'She is married?' Angelina's stare still held some suspicion. After all, it was Matty who had said that Raven had never brought a woman to the house before. She had lied, then . . .

'Surely, child. To Raúl, the captain's first mate. Young fool, saddling himself with a girl like that . . . Nothing in trousers is safe while she is around.'

'Some men would find that most satisfactory.'

'The captain ain't "some men", if that's what you're thinking. He's too patient with her, I always tell him; but then he's a gentleman. Now, I'll fetch you another tray.'

'No.' Angelina's stubborn tone defied argument. 'I meant what I said. Where has Captain Raven gone? I saw him ride away.'

'To the village. Word came early this morning that the damage is bad there. Caleb is loading a wagon now with food and extra blankets, and odd clothes we can spare.'

'Well, you can take all those in the wardrobe,' Angelina told her, and Matty looked at her as if she had taken leave of her senses. 'I won't wear any of them. Is there a horse I can ride?'

The woman nodded, obviously at a loss what to say in the face of this rebellion. Not want all those lovely clothes? The girl was mad, or hurting so bad inside that she needed to hurt someone else to ease the pain.

'Have it saddled for me. And I want a shirt, a man's shirt, and some trousers. And boots.'

'You can't ride about like that! The captain will be furious!'

'Good! It won't be the first time. Please, Matty.' Angelina's tone softened. This woman was the only person who could give her the means to obtain a few hours' peace before the confrontation with Raven, which would find her either forced into his bed, or free to leave the island. 'I need to be alone for a while. I have to think . . . and I like to be comfortable. I wore similar clothes on board the *Sea Witch*, and the captain didn't mind, then.'

'That was different. You're here now,' Matty sniffed, but after only one look into the wide green eyes full of misery, she nodded her huge head. 'I'll find you something. You're about the same height and build as my eldest boy. He's a groom here.'

She went away, and came back some ten minutes later with everything Angelina had asked for. They were not a bad fit, she found, as she hurriedly pulled them on, oblivious of the woman's horrified gaze.

'What time is it? Is Charity awake yet?' Angelina asked, as she pushed her hair out of sight beneath a wide-brimmed straw hat that had also been provided. The clothes in no way hid the fact that she was a woman, but they would allow her the freedom she needed at the moment to roam the island without arousing too much curiosity.

'Awake and gone from the house this hour past,' Matty returned. 'She went on the wagon with Stumpy to help in the village.'

'But she is not well!' Angelina cried in disbelief. 'For the past two weeks she has been on her feet for hardly more than a few minutes at a time. You had no right to allow her to go!'

'That old woman has a mind of her own—as you have,' Matty snorted. 'She looked all right to me. Besides, Stumpy will take good care of her. My man thinks they may tie the knot—maybe.'

'You mean—get married? Charity—and that old pirate? I won't allow it! She's a good, decent woman.'

'And that old man will spend the rest of his days giving her the love she has been missing for so many years. Besides, what do you want with her now? A grown woman . . . with a man of your own? Let her enjoy what days are left to her,' Matty replied, frowning heavily at the girl's indignant features. 'It ain't right you should run her life for her.'

'Is your life your own?' Angelina demanded sharply. 'Or Caleb's? Your son's? Do any of the people here run their own lives, or does Captain Raven tell them what to do, as his spanish predecessor did? You are still slaves . . . All of you.'

'Slaves!' The woman began to laugh, holding on to her enormous waist with tears starting to her eyes. 'Child, wherever did you get that idea? The captain freed us all the day he arrived here. When the Spanish sailed from Jamaica, the Don who lived here—Don Ramón Alvaro, ordered his men to kill us all. He was not going to follow the example of his fellow Spaniards and free us. Oh, no, not him. So we rose up one night—the very night the captain's ship anchored for the first time in the bay—and we killed him. He and his men helped us. Together we rid the island of all Spaniards. Slaves—us! We stay here because it's our home, and a good one now. We are fed, clothed, we have places to live; there is land a-plenty for those who want to work it. The captain has great ideas.

We're as free as you are! Slaves . . .' She left the room, her body still shaking with silent laughter, leaving Angelina lost for words.

They were all free to do as they pleased, to come and go at will—except her. One slave still remained on the island—herself!

As she made her way downstairs, she took a good look at her surroundings, seeing many things which had escaped her notice the night before in her desperation to be out of her wet clothes. The walls were rich with colourful paintings in ornate frames of polished wood or gold fretwork. Thick carpets were scattered over the stone floors, in bright colours and designs pleasing to the eye. With the passing of the hurricane, the shutters had been opened and the windows thrown wide to allow the rooms to air. Sunshine flooded into many that she passed. There were rooms with books, rooms with weapons of every size and description hanging on the walls. Curved scimitars, swords with long blades of the finest Toledo steel. Daggers and slim-bladed stilettos hung side by side with African spears and knurled clubs.

The staircase brought her back into the entrance hall. Off to her left she found a large well-furnished room, the furniture mainly of Spanish style, intermingled with Moorish-designed tables inlaid with brass, and some with silver. More bright cushions were scattered on the long, low sofa which stretched the whole length of an enormous chasm of a fireplace. At least six feet, she estimated, pausing in the doorway to survey the comfort and quiet elegance of the room. She could imagine how cosy it would be to sit before a blazing fire on a cold night . . .

Quickly she turned away, aware of who would be sharing the sofa with her. There was a passage honeycombed with more rooms of varying sizes. She could hear voices coming from somewhere along it, and surmised that it led to the kitchen and perhaps the servants' quarters. As Matty and her family were not slaves, they would sleep in the house.

As she stepped out into the warmth of the brilliant sunshine, the sweet scent of oleanders and wild flowers came to her, the aroma heightened by the heavy rain which had soaked everything the night before. She walked beneath leafy jacaranda trees to the stables, where a young Negro waited for her with a gentle-looking mare.

Angelina thanked him, and placed one foot in his cupped hands to swing herself astride the animal, aware of the growing astonishment on the black face as she wheeled her about and urged her towards the trees at a fast canter. A woman dressed in his clothes . . . and riding astride like a man! He was still gazing at the apparition, scratching his head in bewilderment, as horse and rider disappeared from view. He wondered what the captain would say when he discovered that his lady was riding about the island like some rough-shod peasant boy!

As the trees and bushes closed behind her, concealing her from anyone watching from the house, she slowed her pace to a steady trot and sat back to admire the scenery. She had never ridden astride before and was surprised how comfortable it was, instead of being perched on a high side saddle, weighed down with cumbersome skirts. She would always ride this way. If Raven did not like her attire, he could provide her with more suitable trousers and a silk blouse tailored to fit her more closely than the shirt she had tucked into the waistband of the faded breeches she now had on.

Although, she had to admit, any tight-fitting clothes would have made it impossible to breathe. As it was, she felt a trickle of perspiration run down her back and then from beneath her hat down over the back of her neck.

Wild birds with multi-coloured plumage called to her from the trees. Some shrieked in a perfect imitation of a child crying; others made harsh, guttural noises, as if reprimanding her for intruding into their domain. She heard things scurrying in the bushes, and wondered what kind of animals lurked there. Wild cats, maybe, boar —creeping things like snakes and lizards. She decided she had had enough of the forest, and urged the horse through light brush to gain the edge of the beach.

It was littered with débris: wood and seaweed, dead birds, flotsam from some ship caught in the storm and probably sunk. There was not a sign of another living soul, but the destruction caused by the fierce wind and the torrential rain was plain to see as she rode on. Climbing a bank back on to hard earth again, she gazed across an expanse of cultivated fields. The sun was slowly drying the ruined corn and sweet potatoes, but she doubted if any could be salvaged for use. A few acres, sheltered in the lee of the trees, had survived, but would this be enough to feed the inhabitants of the village? What would Raven do if there was insufficient food for their needs? Take to the sea again, and plunder and rob until he had gained enough?

Further on were more fields, with a few scantily-clad Negroes moving up and down the rows of rain-soaked plants. They watched her pass without speaking or acknowledging her presence in any way, as though they sensed she was a stranger, despite her clothing. She allowed the horse to pick her own way along a narrow path, well trodden by other animals, and was surprised that little or no signs showed of the water, which must surely have flooded over this even ground. Beneath the baking sun, the earth was already beginning to harden and crack.

She lost track of time. Midday perhaps, or later? What did it matter. She was in no hurry to return to the house and face Raven. A sound from some dense oleander bushes to one side of her made her rein in. A whimper, like that of a child in pain. Cautiously she headed into the undergrowth again, and within seconds had come across a half-naked Negro boy sitting on the ground, nursing one ankle.

'Are you hurt?' Eyes as black as jet swept up to where she sat. The young face was definitely hostile, and she gave a soft sigh. Was everyone on the island unfriendly? 'Can I help you?'

'My ankle . . . I fell and twisted it.' The answer was slow in coming. He was perhaps nine or ten years old, with a crop of black curls framing a thin, secretive face. He sent a furtive glance at the face framed beneath the straw hat, then his eyes fastened on the mare Angelina was riding. Perhaps recognising her as coming from the house, he ventured to ask, 'You go village—help us?'

'I don't know where it is. I am a stranger here. If you take my hand and climb up behind me, you can show me where it is. Do you live there?'

Her outstretched hand was ignored. The boy struggled up, but the moment he attempted to place any weight on his injured foot, he sank to the ground again with a low gasp of pain.

'A warrior does not accept help from women,' he declared, with a fierceness of tone that took her aback.

'Then the warrior is very foolish. Would it not be better for him to accept the help offered and live to fight another day?' Angelina glanced meaningfully up at the sky. 'It's a beautiful day now, but perhaps the wind and rain will return after dark. If so, you will be one warrior who is feeling very sorry for himself.'

'You laugh at me!' the boy cried, his hands curling into tight fists as he glared into her softly tanned cheeks. He did not know her, yet she mocked him—Datu, son of Mahommi. The gods would strike her dead for such an insult!

'A little, perhaps, and I apologise. It was not meant unkindly.' For the first time, Angelina noticed a large bunch of greenery lying at his side. Strange-shaped ferns, leafy twigs and small yellow flowers. 'Are those important?'

'They are for my mother to make strong medicine for the injured ones. She is expecting me.' Again he struggled to his feet. Gathering up the bundle, he reluctantly held out his hand for Angelina to help him to mount behind her. 'Perhaps, this once, it is permissible for a warrior to demean himself.'

She held back a smile at the arrogant comment and set off again, with him leaning against her shoulder as he guided her.

'What is your name?'

'I am Datu. I am Dahomey . . .'

And that explained everything, she thought, as he relapsed into silence—but not to her!

Fifteen minutes later they came upon the first of the houses, set beside a water-mill which had been constructed to harness the power of the stream. Being built of stone, it had fared reasonably well, with only a small part of its bamboo roof being damaged. Further on, however, most of the dwellings, little more than wooden huts, some on stilts to avoid any flooding which might occur when the river burst its bank and swirled down the main street, had been flattened by the winds.

Main street! It was little more than a dirt track now —full of broken beams and bamboo, shattered furniture, cooking utensils . . . the contents of the villagers' homes. People were working like beavers amid the wreckage. Women gathered what was necessary to keep body and soul together while their men set about the more difficult, if not impossible task, to her mind, of repairing what was left of their battered dwellings. Out of fifteen or sixteen houses, only three were totally intact because they had been constructed in stone. Six more, partially demolished, were being used to house the injured, to set up some kind of kitchen to feed nourishment to hungry men and women, to give shelter to those with no roofs over their heads for the coming night.

All were working as though they had a dozen pairs of hands, she saw with mounting incredulity and admiration for the swift way the situation was being coped with. As she pulled up, she glimpsed Raven disappearing into one of the demolished houses. He reappeared, in his arms the broken form of a child whom he gave to a weeping woman to be borne away, and then was gone again. He was stripped to the waist, sweat gleaming on his brown chest. He really did care for these people, she thought, wishing she could be of some help, but not knowing how to go about making the offer.

'Datu! Son, where have you been? Your mother has been waiting for those herbs a good hour.' A tall black figure stood beside Angelina's horse. Datu scrambled from her back, biting back the gasp of pain which rose to his lips as his foot touched the ground. A warrior did not cry out—at least not before his father, she saw, impressed by the boy's courage.

'I found him some way back; he has injured his ankle,' she ventured to say, and found herself totally ignored as Datu spoke to the man in a strange tongue.

'Come—you are welcome in my house . . . What is left of it,' she was told, and the tall Negro motioned to a hut, barely standing, a few yards away. Sensing that it would be rude to refuse the invitation, she slipped from the saddle and followed them inside.

There were two rooms, partioned by a bright curtain drawn back to show her what had once been a bedroom. The roof of straw and bamboo had collapsed upon the wooden structures, completely demolishing them. The one in which she stood had fared little better. Cooking utensils were strewn across the floor; crockery was smashed. The only survivors were roughly-hewn wooden bowls, which a woman was gathering together. She quickly came to her feet as the three of them entered, and a look of astonishment crossed the pretty dusky face as she stared at Angelina's strange garb.

'This is my wife, Elani. I am Mahommi. Have we nothing to offer our guest, woman? She has been kind to our son.'

'Nothing . . . I was just going for fresh water.'

'Please, you have more than enough to do here without an unwanted visitor,' Angelina protested, as Mahommi sent a baleful glare at his wife. Even under these circumstances, he expected the poor woman to furnish food and drink for guests. Obviously another warrior! 'I am pleased that I could help. Can I do more here? Can I bring you things you need from the house . . . Captain Raven's house,' she added, to tell him where she had come from.

'I know where you are from. It is good the captain has found himself a woman at last. You will give him many fine sons . . . to become warriors like Datu. Warriors of the Dahomey, so that we never forget what we are,' the man commented.

Angelina's cheeks flooded with colour. Did the whole village know of her arrival, and why she had been brought to the island?

'It is our wish that our son should be as his forefathers were, brave and courageous in battle. A warrior like my father—the warrior I was never allowed to be,' Mahommi added, his voice growing bitter.

'We were stolen from our homes ten years ago, sold like cattle and brought to this island,' Elani explained. 'We have been beaten and starved, and humiliated, but our spirits have not been broken.'

'You are free now, so why do you not return home?' Angelina asked, impressed by the pride of these people and their desire to cling to their proud heritage.

'We have a good life here,' the woman replied, with a shrug of slim shoulders. 'We shall have many more children, and they will be Dahomey warriors—just as if we were still in our own land. The captain has set us free, given us new life here. That is why we are so pleased he has brought you to be by his side. It is not good for a man to be alone. Tonight in my prayers, I will ask the gods to bless you with many boy children. You will find favour in their eyes, for you have a kind heart.'

'Th-Thank you.' Angelina dared not ask to whom she prayed, but knew they were unlikely to be Christian gods. These people were too steeped in their past history and glory to accept a new religion in the place of the old. 'I—I really would like to help, if I can . . . Anything.'

'Come, you can pound the herbs for me while I prepare the mixture. First we tend Datu's ankle, and then we take the rest to the injured. Many have open wounds which will get worse in this heat if we do not treat them properly.'

Gathering up the bundle Datu had brought, she led Angelina to a small table which had somehow miraculously survived the roof falling in to one side of it, and laid on it several bowls and some thick, short sticks.

'A different bowl for each herb, you understand? They must be crushed so that the juices flow.'

Angelina nodded. Pulling off her hat, she set to work, unaware of the way Mahommi stared in awe at the long red hair before he turned and left them. Elani's English was not as good as Jacquetta's, but as Angelina worked and talked with her, she found it quite comprehensible. Raven had insisted that they all learn at least the basics of the language, telling them they would be cheated and ridiculed if they chose to leave the island at any time and could not speak the white man's tongue. He wanted them to read and write, too, she discovered; but many of the older men and women were too set in their ways to pay any attention to learning more. The younger ones, with encouragement, could be taught, Elani told her, but so far, they had not managed to build a schoolhouse, and the only man who came to instruct them had been frightened back to the mainland by a hurricane such as the one that had hit the island the previous night.

Angelina came to understand there was so much more to Raven than she had ever thought possible. He sailed the high seas, committing mayhem, plundering, yet he sought to give these ex-slaves a better way of life without taking away from them their own identity. She comprehended the need to keep that. Here, on the island, she did have a kind of freedom, she realised. She could do so much for these people, and assist him in his enormous undertaking. Assist him? Was she mad? Why should she help an amoral, womanising pirate who had lied to her and betrayed her passionate longing for him? But she would. She knew it was inevitable. The island had reached out and claimed her for its own—as Raven had. She would never leave. Nor would she allow another woman near him again. If she were to be his mistress, she would be his only mistress . . . the only woman in his life. She would satisfy him so that he had no need to seek his pleasures elsewhere.

'Why do you smile?' Elani asked, looking at her curiously.

'Because I am happy.' Happy? Her heart soared as free as a bird. Never had she known such sweet peace of mind, such contentment. If this was the joy one felt when loving another, she had been a fool to deny herself the pleasure for so long.

For another hour she meticulously pounded the concoction of herbs Elani handed to her. This accomplished, she watched the woman add them to a mixture already prepared over a fire outside. A liberal amount was spread on Datu's ankle before they left to attend to those injuried in the night's havoc.

From the way Elani was spoken to and the respect shown to her whomever she talked to, Angelina came to realise she was someone of importance in the village. Here and there a coin was offered for her services —money seemed to be the only commodity that had survived intact—but she always shook her head, declining payment.

A blistering sun sweltered above them as they worked. Tired men threw themselves down by the wayside to rest, and were brought food and drink, mainly rum mixed with water to revive their flagging spirits. Angelina looked for Raven, but could see no sign of him. She wanted to talk to him, to tell him what was in her heart . . .

'What do you want here? You are not welcome,' a sibilant voice hissed in her ear, as she left Elani to wander in search of him. Jacquetta came from one of the houses to walk at her side, her face taut with anger. 'Why do you not escape? I shall help you.'

'I have no intention of leaving the island. I have changed my mind,' Angelina returned quietly. Green eyes glinted with anger as she stared into the other's face. 'Go away. Leave my man alone! If you don't, I shall forget I am a lady, and scratch out your eyes.'

'He wants me . . . You will see! You will be sorry!'

In a flurry of frilled petticoats, she flounced away, but Angelina had seen the uncertainty which leapt into her eyes, and was pleased.

She stopped to look into each place where there were people, often getting caught up in the slow, painstaking process of bandaging injured limbs, and generally making herself useful. The hours passed, and she began to feel the strain of it all herself, not realising until a wave of giddiness passed over her that she had eaten nothing since the night before.

A rosy-cheeked woman passed her, carrying a bundle of cloths, and peered into her strained face.

'Are you all right, dearie?' She had a broad London accent, one Angelina had heard many times along the docks at Tilbury and Wapping. 'You look all in! Come along with Meg, and I'll find you a nice mug of tea. Wine, if you prefer. Thank the good Lord, a few of our precious barrels survived, or we would be in a pretty pickle.'

Angelina did not object as her arm was taken and she was led beneath the shade of enormous jacaranda trees, where men and women were clustered round a fire. From a cauldron, there came an appetising aroma of stew that made her stomach crawl with hunger. Most of the men were resting while their wives or sweethearts —even their daughters, she thought, looking at some of the young faces—tore sheets and tablecloths into makeshift bandages. And sitting with them was Charity, chattering away to the woman beside her as if she had known her all her life.

'Charity, thank goodness I have found you!' Angelina sank down beside her and could not stop herself from giving the woman a fierce hug. 'When Matty told me you had left the house, I was so worried'—although she had had little time since to dwell on it, she thought a trifle ashamedly. Her first priority should have been to find Charity and take her back. Yet she did not look tired, or unduly disturbed by being with strangers. As Angelina drew back from her and gratefully accepted the tin mug thrust into her hands, Charity turned and smiled at her—such a warm, content smile, and she knew she had nothing to worry about.

'Sorry it's not bone china, dearie, but we've run out,' Meg said cheerfully, returning to her place beside the fire. Angelina was about to ask if she might have a little of the stew, when a man rose up on one elbow and glared across at her.

'What does she want? The captain won't like his fancy piece gettin' her lily white hands dirty!'

'That's enough from you, Josh Appleford. What are you still doing here anyway, you lazy scum? Get back to work with the others.' Meg rounded on him, brandishing a large wooden spoon, and the man scrambled to his feet, swearing as he backed away. 'And watch your language, or the captain will hear of it. She's a lady

—and I mean a real lady not used to your kind of foul talk.'

'It's all right, Meg,' Angelina said, deliberately ignoring the man's outburst. 'I come from a long line of seafaring men, and I do admit to hearing some blood-curdling oaths in my time from Grandfather and Father. Not to mention my crews, when they forgot I was about!'

'Fancy you being captain of a ship! Lawd, whatever possessed you?' a young woman asked in awe of the boyish figure sitting cross-legged beside her. 'Beggin' your pardon for being so rude as to ask.'

'My father was in ill health and unable to run the business properly. I stepped into his shoes as a son would have done, that's all. And after he died, it was necessary to continue for a while. I do not regret a moment of it.' Angelina realised that everyone knew about her, yet it did not matter. They seemed to accept her among them.

'You should have seen her at the wheel of the *Sea Witch*,' a voice remarked mockingly to the rear. Raúl sauntered into view, showing no surprise at either her presence among them or her clothes. 'And the capitán watching like the cat who has just stolen the cream! I think he was proud of his capitán in petticoats!'

Angelina almost choked over her tea at the remark, which brought smiles to many faces around her. She sipped the hot liquid, and drew back startled. It contained neither milk nor very much sugar, from the taste of it. It was not at all what she was accustomed to.

'That's how we drink it here,' Raúl told her, still grinning.

'A slice of lemon and only a little sugar. It is refreshing, no?'

Conscious of all eyes on her, Angelina downed the

contents of the tin mug. She had to admit that it was, indeed, very refreshing.

'I think I am going to like it here,' Charity murmured, and she rounded on her in open-mouthed surprise. 'My mind is at peace in this beautiful place. Strange, is it not? Jason is such a wonderful young man.'

She spoke of him as a son, Angelina thought. Edgar had always been 'Lord Edgar'. Never had she been so informal with him.

'Have you no wish to go home to England? To all our friends?'

'I feel something very bad will happen if I do. I like it here, and Jason has said I may make it my home if I wish. Which, of course it will be if I marry that old reprobate Stumpy . . . He asked me last night, you know.'

'Charity!' Angelina sat back on her heels, momentarily lost for words, conscious of some amused glances being passed to and fro about her. Yet for all his roughness of manner and speech, was the old man not kind and thoughtful? Charity deserved a little love and affection in her life, as Matty had told her. For so long she had given it to others, and now it was time to receive and to spend the rest of her life being looked after. 'I am very happy for you. Truly I am! I wish you every happiness.'

'Yes, I think I shall be very happy. It will be so nice to have a home of my own, a man to care for. You don't need me any more. You have your own man now.'

'You shall have the best wedding this island has ever seen,' Angelina declared, her eyes suddenly misty. 'I shall take you to Jamaica to shop for a fine trousseau.' At which Charity laughed, thinking of being fitted out in frills and fripperies at her time of life. 'And I shall buy something to remind you of me when you are alone with your Stumpy. Something which says thank you for all your wisdom and patience.'

'A present . . .' For a moment Charity's eyes had that far-away look again, and Angelina wondered if she was drifting back into the past, slipping away from her as she had done so often on the *Sea Witch*. But then she smiled, and said quite lucidly, 'I have just the thing for you. I have treasured it for many years, ever since the day my dearest Drusilla gave it to me. It was the last thing she ever gave me . . .' Her lips quivered, but she recovered herself and continued, 'It is a small onyx jewel-box. Quite an exquisite piece of workmanship. I believe Jason gave it to her in the first place as birthday present. It is fitting that you should have it.'

'Oh, no, Charity. Not if it means so much to you.'

'It is time I put the past behind me. I am sure now that my memory is lost for ever. I must accept it. Yes, Angelina . . . You shall have the box tomorrow.'

As it began to grow dark, fires were lighted throughout the village. Lanterns hung from the trees, and makeshift shelters erected beneath them became filled with weary bodies seeking rest after their hard labours. Groups clustered together to talk. Some just sat and mourned the four people killed when buildings had collapsed, among them the small child Angelina had seen in Raven's arms. A few sang to revive flagging spirits; the minister prayed; and from somewhere in the vastness of the forest beyond came the sound of drums. How resourceful these people were, she marvelled, looking about her. Black and white, living and working together in harmony. The society she had known would be appalled by such a spectacle!

As she turned to ask someone about the drums, a tall

figure materialised from the shadows to stand before her. All the things she had been practising in her mind as she worked, to say to him now, vanished at the sight of Raven's tired features. He was still without a shirt. His breeches were badly cut in places; blood had long since dried against the material. His hands, too, were scratched and bloodstained. His face was streaked with dirt and sweat.

His eyes searched her face, noting the weariness in her also. 'How long have you been here?'

'Hours. I don't really know. I brought back a boy called Datu . . . He had hurt his ankle,' she explained. She wanted him to hold her so much that she ached.

'Mahommi's lad? No wonder the drums are beating. They are for you,' he added, seeing her puzzlement. 'Mahommi's wife is the High Priestess here. The drums are asking the voodoo gods to smile on the woman with red hair whose heart is as pure as the sunlight, as rich with kindness as a chest of gold. Do you no longer find us barbarians, Angelina? Bloodthirsty pirates? Has my island captivated the heart that I cannot?' There was an oddness about his tone that made her look at him sharply, but his features were darkened by shadows.

'It is the most beautiful place I have ever seen,' she murmured. 'I shall never leave . . . but I shall not play second fiddle to another woman!' Her eyes flared with warning as she spoke, and Raven's mouth gaped as he stared at her.

Then, with a loud chuckle, he swung her up into his arms and turned towards the dark mass of trees ahead. As they passed a group of men drinking heartily from a large barrel, one of them snatched up a leather bottle from the ground and tossed it in their direction.

'Compliments of us all, Capt'n,' he called, and grinned wickedly as Raven deftly caught it.

'We'll remember to drink your health, friend,' came the low, amused reply.

'Where are you taking me? Put me down at once! We have to talk,' Angelina insisted. 'Besides they will think . . . Well . . . You can imagine!'

'Indeed I can. That I want to be alone with you. They are right. Isn't that what you want? Or am I going to have more trouble with you?' Raven demanded, shifting his hold so that she was held more closely against his bare chest. He smelt of sweat and wood-smoke, but she did not care. His lips touched her cheek and found her mouth, bruising them with the unleashing of his pent-up passions. 'When I've cleaned this grime from me, then we'll talk,' he said, setting her down beside the stream. He had carried her almost to the mill, well out of sight and hearing of those behind. He gestured towards the water. 'Will you not join me?'

'I think I would prefer to wait until we get back to the house,' Angelina returned, hurriedly turning her back as he began to strip off his boots and breeches. As there came a soft splash, she looked round to find him washing himself at the water's edge. In the few short hours she had been in the village, the stream had returned to no more than its normal height. Even in the half light, she could see the muscles rippling across the broad back as he bent to wash the dirt from his legs and carefully examine the many cuts and grazes there.

She averted her gaze again as he came clambering out to seek his clothes, and did not look up again until he threw himself down beside her on the ground, water still dripping from his crisp black hair.

'It is settled, then? You are mine?' He did not know

what had happened to make her change her mind so suddenly, only that it took precedence over everything: even the tiredness which dogged his limbs and the gnawing hunger in his stomach, for, like Angelina, he had not eaten all day.

She nodded, adding sharply, 'If you dare to gloat, I—I will hit you!'

'I would not do that. I am pleased you have come to your senses. What did Edgar give you as a wedding gift?' he asked suddenly.

'A carriage.' Why did he speak of Edgar at such a time? She wanted nothing to spoil her cloudless horizons.

'In which to take the air when you grew bored or lonely or he was otherwise engaged with his numerous women. I shall give you something far more meaningful. A ruby the size of a pigeon's egg. When I look into it, I see the smouldering fires such as I know dwell within you and which I shall soon arouse! That will be *my* gift to *you*.'

'I don't want it—it was probably stolen,' she lied feebly.

'From a maharaja's treasure-chest, actually. It was the most priceless item he possessed. He kept it in a box. I shall give it a worthwhile setting,' Raven chuckled, wicked lights dancing in his eyes.

If he had not mentioned Edgar and brought him into her thoughts again when she had so pointedly dismissed him from them, and revived the past and all the ugliness it contained, Angelina knew she would never have dared to ask her next question. Even as the words left her mouth, she knew it was the wrong thing to do.

'Will you not tell me what happened between you?' she begged.

'No,' Raven said flatly, stiffening where he sat. He had been about to touch her, but now he drew back, his eyes narrowing.

'Do you fear my judgment so much?'

'Judgment?' he thundered, and she flinched at the undertones of fury she could hear. How swiftly he could change! 'What right have you to judge me? God knows there were others willing enough to point the finger. Edgar sowed his seeds of mistrust so cunningly that even poor Drusilla was ensnared before she realised it. I am Raven the pirate. It is he who kidnapped you and brought you here. He who desires you in his bed. Jason Sarandon no longer exists. My brother did not take as much from me as he imagined.'

'Only your proud name—your home—the right to hold up your head among decent people,' she whispered, tears springing to her eyes.

'I have a new name and a new home,' he told her grimly. 'I am well respected here. Do you realise that you have not questioned my words, Angelina? Why do you not leap to Edgar's defence? Are you beginning to wonder just a little about him?'

She blenched at the mocking taunt. She had brought this pain upon herself, and the blame was hers alone. 'Until you tell me otherwise, I must believe the facts as he gave them to me,' she persisted weakly.

'Facts? Only he and I know what took place the night she was attacked—that dreadful night she was killed. She sent for me, but I—God help me—arrived too late to save her. And Charity, that dear sweet soul, who has suffered much because of us both. I will not have her hurt any more. That is all I shall say on this matter. Do you understand me?'

'Yes.' Her voice was barely audible. His fingers

touched a wet cheek, and she heard an expletive explode under his breath.

'Do you think me capable of such brutality? Do you?'

'No . . . I'm sorry.' She fell against his chest, the tears coursing down over the hand which gently cupped her cheek. 'We shall speak of it no more, I promise.'

She lifted her face to his, seeking to blot out the unpleasantness which had come between them. The touch of Raven's lips erased the past and Edgar in an instant. He crushed her beneath him on the sun-baked earth, and she no longer held back from him as he began to rouse her, as if to show him that she believed in him and trusted in him. When he eased himself away from her, she lay trembling in his arms, her cheeks flushed, lips quivering from his kisses.

'Much as I would like to stay here,' Raven whispered, nibbling her ear until she squirmed in pleasure, 'I am going to take you back to the house. But don't think I am always going to play the gentleman, my angel. If we did not have so much work still to be done here tomorrow, I should not be so gallant now. As soon as we can be alone together . . . undisturbed . . .' A night bird swooped through the trees above them, and he gave a short laugh. 'There are eyes everywhere, watching us I imagine, and I am not one to make my love-making a public spectacle.'

There were knowing smiles and glances as they returned to the village and found their horses. Raven grinned back at his men, while Angelina pretended to notice nothing amiss, although her cheeks were burning with embarrassment by the time they rode away. Raven was to return the following morning at first light to help with the repairs. Although she wanted to help, Angelina knew she might not be out of her bed until midday. She was reeling with tiredness by the time they reined in before the house, and came sliding out of the saddle into Raven's waiting arms.

'Your dress sense is atrocious,' he remarked, as she nestled her head against his bare shoulder. 'I want to come back tomorrow to a woman who looks like a woman, not a boy.'

As he carried her into the hall and started towards the stairs, the door to the drawing-room opened, and a man stepped out. Both Raven and Angelina stared at the immaculately-clad figure, as surprised by his sudden appearance as he was by the bedraggled girl with red hair, dressed in boy's attire, being carried in the arms of a half-naked man. Raven set her down, his face breaking into a broad smile.

'Seth! You made it on time . . . I'd forgotten! Forgive me?'

'Now there's a fine welcome! I set sail in the aftermath of a howling gale to come here, bringing you all the fripperies and whatnots you stated must arrive by the fifteenth—and what happens? You forgot I was coming. Do you get married every day?'

'Forgive me, my old friend.' Raven shook his hand warmly, then slipped an arm about his shoulders as he looked into Angelina's startled features. She had met this man in Port Royal! He was the very same with whom she had negotiated a profitable contract. A friend of Raven! Was this his informant? Of course, it must be. Lord Seth Courtney and Jason Sarandon together! An ill-matched pair—or were they? 'The hurricane all but devastated the village. We have been working there all day. Are your men still on board? I could make use of them.'

'You shall have them first thing in the morning.'

'My thanks. Damnation, I'm so tired that I am forgetting my manners. But then introductions are unnecessary, are they not? You know each other. Do you remember Seth Courtney, angel? The best friend I have ever had.'

Raven had watched her at Lord Courtney's ball, she remembered. They had conspired together! Despite the tiredness which dogged her, her beauty was still evident, and the older man was regarding her with open admiration, oblivious of the anger beginning to rise in her face.

'I am delighted to meet you again, Miss Blackthorne.' He touched her fingers to his lips with a courteous bow. 'If I was a gambling man, I would have wagered that Jason could never have pulled this off. Why, he even made all the wedding arrangements before he sailed to—meet you.' At last, aware of the frustrated anger and humiliation mounting inside her, he added softly, 'Oh dear, have you done something rash, my boy? The young lady seems rather annoyed.'

'I rather fear I have, Seth. I have stolen my brother's bride. I should have done so, no matter whom she was betrothed to, but as it is Edgar I am hurting, the risk was well worth it. I am in the process of trying to steal her heart, too. Perhaps you can put in a good word for me?'

'You are well able to speak for yourself. I had not realised . . . What will your brother do? Send men to get her back?'

'Him? Never! Besides, if one of his ships shows herself here, I shall blow her out of the water. I've cannon placed all round the headland for just such an occasion.'

Angelina gasped at the threat. The magic she had shared with Raven until now was rapidly fading. Once again she felt the hatred in his voice as he spoke of his brother. Although she would never broach the subject again with him, Edgar would always live in his heart, haunting him.

'We shall change, and then join you again, Seth,' Raven said, looking down at his attire—or rather the lack of it. 'And then we shall all drink a toast to my future wife.'

Angelina's gasp brought all eyes to her face.

'Wife?' What had she had heard? That he intended to marry her? Lord Courtney had been serious? Wedding arrangements? Her mind reeled with questions which would not pass her lips while Raven grinned at her so wickedly.

'But of course, my dear. I have a ship full of gifts —furniture and the like for the bride. And, of course, the most magnificent wedding gown ever created . . . or so the woman who made it told me,' Seth chuckled. 'Surely this young man . . . Raven! You dog! The poor girl doesn't know?'

Angelina turned and ran before they saw the confusion, the shame which flooded into her face. His bride! Wedding dress! He had planned it from the very beginning, yet had said nothing to her. Raven started towards the stairs, then halted, a frown on his dark features. For the moment he knew it was best to leave her to accept this sudden news. It was not the way he had intended to break it to her, but it was done now, and he would just have to accept the consequences of his heavy-handedness.

Matty stared in amazement at the tearful girl who rushed into the room, slamming the door behind her, and threw herself over the bed, her face in her hands.

'Lordy, child. What's wrong? What a state you are in. Are you hurt?' Her voice trailed off as Angelina lifted her head. Her eyes, brimming with tears, but not tears of anger, or pain—they were tears of joy!

'He is going to make me his wife, Matty! He wants to marry me.'

'Of course he does, child. What on earth did you think?'

Angelina threw her arms about the matronly form, and hugged her with such enthusiasm that the woman collapsed on to the bed beside her.

CHAPTER
TEN

As MATTY was brushing Angelina's hair some time later, while, attired in a soft robe, her body still glowing from a hot, relaxing bath she sat dreaming her own secret thoughts on a stool before the dressing table, a commotion sounded outside the door. As both women turned towards it, it was flung open and Caleb lurched in, his muscles bulging from the weight of the two brassbound chests he carried, one under each arm. He set them down in the middle of the room, and left with a knowing grin at his wife.

Angelina sat speechless as Raven entered, bearing a smaller chest. She had not thought she would see him again until morning, for she had sent word that she would sup in her room and retire early after the day's exertions. She needed time to think, to absorb the great shock he had delivered without warning. His wife! Even now, she could hardly believe that the words had come from his lips.

He was attired in clean breeches of dark blue velvet, cut snugly against his lean thighs. A brilliant white shirt of the finest silk, with a froth of lace of his throat, accentuated the swarthiness of his skin. Part pirate, with a touch of gentleman thrown in, she mused. He would never be anything else in her eyes. Which was the stronger: the breeding and background he had left behind in England, or the ruthless way of life he now accepted as inevitable?

'Leave us, Matty,' he ordered.

'She has not finished my hair!' Angelina protested, but the door was already closing behind the woman's rounded rear.

'As I am leaving at first light tomorrow, I thought it better if we settled things between us now,' Raven said matter-of-factly, as he set down the chest in front of her. 'You said you would not marry me for a chest of treasure, so I offered two. Here they are. The third is thrown in for good measure.'

The insult momentarily robbed her of breath, and then she came to her feet, fists clenched, drew one back and aimed it at his grinning face. With a deep-throated chuckle, he grabbed her wrists and pulled her into his arms to kiss her soundly, until the hands that had been raised to strike him were locked about his neck and the anger had drained from her, leaving her flustered and searching for words.

'You—You beast! You inhuman monster!' Colour suffused her cheeks as his amusement grew. Devilish lights twinkled in the grey eyes which stared down into her indignant features.

'Because I bring you a dowry fit for a queen? Nay, two queens?' And then his smile faded slightly as he realised the anguish which had been haunting her day and night since he had taken her from the *White Swan*. 'You are right, no gentleman would have subjected a lady to the torture you have endured these past weeks . . . But you seemed so determined to fight me at every turn, that I dared show no leniency—no affection—for you, my angel, lest you thought it a weakness in me and sought to turn it to your advantage.'

Angelina began to relax in his embrace as she absorbed his words. Affection! Was he saying he *cared* for her? She lifted a hand to smooth her loose hair back from her face, and as she did so he smelt the fragrance of her skin, still damp from her bath. At the tender expression which crept into his eyes, the way his hand slid round to her back, caressing her through the robe, she was left in no doubt that he did have some feelings for her . . .

'Am I to share your—affections, sir? With Jacquetta?'

'Matty told me she was talking to you this morning. That wench is a fool. One day Raúl will kill her if she continues to taunt him with her casual affairs. There is nothing between us, although she dogs my footsteps whenever I am near the village. She was a maid here once, helping Matty, but she became such a nuisance flaunting herself under my nose that I sent her packing,' Raven answered, with a sincerity of tone that left her in no doubt as to the truth of his words. 'I have never touched her.'

'I saw you kissing her . . .'

'No! She kissed me, and earned herself the sharp end of my tongue for her foolishness. Perhaps she hoped you were watching. Why, angel, are you jealous when another woman finds me attractive, and would not hesitate to accept what you have been offered and refused?'

'You offered me your bed, not a ring,' Angelina reminded him, and he nodded slowly.

'That I did, but one always went with the other.'

His words brought a tiny gasp to her lips. He bent his head and kissed them for a long moment, until she pulled herself free—determined that he should tell her all.

'You have no heart to allow me to believe I was to be brought here to be your mistress—your plaything. I have been threatened—coerced—mistreated!' Raven's laughter interrupted her, and once again her wrath disappeared. What was the use of being angry with him now? She had more than she had ever hoped for.

'I gave you to understand no such thing,' he chided gently. 'Only that I would have you. You have a very suspicious little mind, but it is a tiny flaw in such perfection that I can overlook it—and I love you none the less for it.'

The room reeled unsteadily about her. Had he not been holding her tightly against his chest, Angelina wondered if this additional shock might not have made her swoon.

'Love me?' she echoed faintly.

'I lost my heart to you that first day in Port Royal. I've wanted to tell you a thousand times, but I wanted to show you Eden first. That is what I call my island. I brought my ship here in the teeth of a howling gale . . . not unlike the one which welcomed you. When we were safe here, together, where nothing can touch us, I intended to tell you the truth. Once I was sure that you would not turn and run from me.'

'Then or now, it matters not,' Angelina murmured, laying her head against his shoulder. The fierce thudding of her heart beneath his hand matched his own. 'Raven, or Jason Sarandon, I shall love you both always.'

'Have I achieved the impossible?' Raven asked gently, turning her face up to his. 'Have I won the heart of the fairest jewel that was ever seen in the Caribbean? Will there be fair winds in Eden from now on, my love? No more stormy passages for either of us?'

'Indeed you have. With some help from your friends,' she added. 'It was Lord Courtney who supplied you with your information, was it not?'

'So you remembered him. I thought you had. Ay,

Seth's an old friend, and a business partner. It was in his interest as well as mine to know all about you. You concluded a timber contract with him, didn't you on that visit?'

'Why, yes. My price was fair, and he accepted it.'

'On my behalf,' Raven said smilingly. 'The timber you carried to England was mine . . . from this island. I have a fleet of fine ships, which I shall show you when we visit Jamaica. Fishing-smacks provide ample food for Port Royal and the smaller villages close by. I have larger vessels, which trade with the islands that you visited before we—encountered each other. And I have ships which sail to the colonies and bring back an abundance of fine goods to be sold throughout the Caribbean. Raven raised his ugly head only when one of my brother's ships sailed into port . . . or a Spanish treasure galleon ventured too close to my shores. I gave up sailing with Morgan a year past. I did tell you that I was not the blackguard you believed.'

'Then you are doubly heartless to have frightened me so!'

'You! Frightened of me! A reed of a girl who has commanded the respect of a ship's crew, and sailed the high seas like an old salt?'

'That is different. I was always sure of myself and what I was doing, and my reasons. But you . . .' Angelina caught her breath at the gleam which sprang to his eyes. 'You confused me, frightened me, and made me even doubt sometimes that I was a woman!'

'Never doubt that!' he laughed softly as he kissed the lobe of her ear and trailed kisses down to her throat. She trembled in his arms as his touch awakened her, and darts of red-hot flame seared her body. If he took her now, she knew she would not try to prevent it.

'I think it wise that you should marry me soon,' he murmured, his lips travelling still further, to caress the smoothness of a bare shoulder and seek the firm roundness of her breast above the robe. 'Tomorrow should see most of the work done, or as much as can be done before we have felled more timber and quarried stone from the valley on the far side of the island. When the houses are built again, they will withstand any winds. With the aid of Seth's men, we shall be finished by late evening.'

'And I shall have Matty prepare a feast for when you return. A celebration,' she promised, her eyes shining at the prospect of gowning and perfuming herself, to play hostess at his table.

'And you shall wed me the day after, or I shall die of hunger for you.'

'Yes! Oh, yes.' She, too, had done with waiting.

It was some while before Angelina raised her head from his shoulder and looked down at the three seachests that lay open before them. Raven had drawn her down into a chair across his lap, and for a considerable time, nothing had existed but the wonder of their newly-discovered love. Her body ached with the longing to be possessed, and she knew, by the passionate kisses rained on her face and lips and the hands that devastated her through the velvet robe, that he was only a heartbeat away from relinquishing his self-control.

'If you want me . . .' she began, hesitantly, and shyly.

'Want you, woman! Of course I do,' he groaned softly. 'But I'll not spoil our wedding night. I have been patient as long as this . . .'

He watched her eyes shine as her gaze returned to the fits he had brought her. He had never thought it possible for one woman to entrap him so completely, yet Angelina had, and there would not be a day when he did not thank God for it. He could give her everything she wanted—except his name. How that secretly irked him. It was her right!

The first chest had contained bolts of cloth, the finest materials she had ever seen. Cloth of gold and silver, the sheerest muslins and the most exquisite Spanish lace. And linen, everything she would need in the house, all embroidered with the initials 'R' and 'A' skilfully entwined. The initials of the previous owner of the house, Raven reminded her, as she opened the second chest to discover a veritable treasure of silver and gold plate, pewter mugs and tableware, fine-cut glass of every shape and description, all bearing the same initials. He had ordered his initials to be placed on everything he owned, but had been forced to leave before the command was carried out. Women from the village had completed the task of embroidering the linen, and personal items such as underwear and nightgowns in dark red thread, and craftsmen in Jamaica had undertaken the silverware and other items—at Raven's request this time.

For her, Angelina realised, her heart overflowing with love and gratitude. Their initials would be forever entwined as one—as would their hearts. She no longer had any doubt about that fact.

The smallest of the chests had contained more jewels, which took her breath away, for they were even more priceless than those he had given her on board the *Sea Witch*. On the top of the shimmering gems lay a ruby the size of a pigeon's egg indeed, on a heavy gold chain which held ten more smaller rubies, five on either side. It would be worn on her wedding day, she promised herself. Worn in love and with pride as she stood beside him.

As if all these things had not been sufficient, there had

been one final item. Her wedding gown. It lay across a chair beside them, creamy lace and satin with tiers of frothy white petticoats, which would have been the envy of every woman at King Charles's court. She did not mind that it would not be on show for them to see—that only Lord Courtney, apart from the minister and the men and women from the village, would see her dressed so regally. A different way of life had brought her new, different friends. Loyal friends, she hoped, who would like her in the years to come as deeply as they did Raven.

Her eyelids drooped tiredly. They had drunk several glassed of wine together, and she stifled a yawn with a rueful smile.

'Come, it is time you were in bed—and that I left you,' he said, rising. She nestled in his arms, not wanting him to let her go, but he deposited her firmly on the bed and would have drawn away, had she not held him fast.

'I love you,' she whispered, and he slipped down beside her to devour the softness of her lips and enjoy the warmth of her body moulded beneath his, one more time.

'You are a temptress, my angel. A veritable witch!'

'I shall enslave you for ever, and cast a spell over you so that you never leave me.'

'Perhaps it is you who may wish to leave me,' Raven said softly, and she laid a finger across his mouth as a shadow crossed his face, knowing for a moment that his thoughts were once more on the past.

'Nay, my love. I am your captive for ever. You will have to put up with me,' she whispered happily.

'If I must—I must.' This time he did resist her attempt to detain him further and gently disengaged himself from her arms. 'I shall send Matty to you. Sleep well. Tomorrow we shall celebrate in great style. I shall send kegs of rum to the village—the poor devils deserve a rest after what they have been through. And I want them to dance at our wedding. Shall you mind?'

'So long as you do not desert me for some wench with bold, wandering eyes,' Angelina said with a glint in her own, and he laughed as he reached the door.

'Cast your spell then, witch. Hold me fast.'

'I shall,' she whispered to the empty room. 'I shall.'

Despite her exertions of the day before, Angelina awoke early and surprised Matty by appearing downstairs for breakfast. Seth Courtney rose to greet her as she entered, and touched her fingers to his lips in a gesture which brought a warm smile to her face.

'I did not expect to see you until this evening, Miss Blackthorne,' he said, as Caleb pulled out a chair for her to seat herself before he retired. 'Jason seemed to think you would sleep the morning through.'

'Don't you mean Raven?' Angelina asked sweetly. 'The man to whom you gave information about me to enable him to abduct me at sea?'

'My dear young lady, what else could I do? He convinced me that he was lovesick for want of you . . .' Seth's ruddy cheeks glowed with embarrassment at her directness. He studied the slender figure in pale green silk who helped herself to a liberal helping of sliced melon and poured tea for them both, when he nodded his assent to his cup being replenished, with the skill of an accomplished hostess. 'I can quite understand his eagerness. If I were ten years younger, he might well have competition. Am I forgiven for my part in the conspiracy?'

Angelina eyed him in silence for a while. She liked the

man who had taken her under his wing in Jamaica, was grateful for the profitable contract, and grateful to him for enabling Raven to snatch her from the *White Swan*. Had he not done so, she would be almost back in England, to marry a man she did not love. Tomorrow she would stand at the side of a man she adored, and worshipped with every breath in her body. Past suspicions were cast into the darkness recesses of her mind. She loved him. She trusted him!

'I am too happy to be angry with you, Lord Courtney. You see, I do remember you. There I was, thinking myself so clever to obtain such a valuable shipping contract, and all the time Raven had made it possible! The two of you are a pair of rogues. I shall forget your part in the masquerade only if you consent to give me away. I have no one else.'

'My dear child, it will be a pleasure.' He watched with some amusement as Matty appeared and, despite her protests, began to pile eggs, accompanied by wedges of bread, on to Angelina's plate.

'Stop!' she protested laughingly. 'I shall not fit into my wedding gown.'

'It's only one day away child. I ain't going to put that much on you in such a short time,' the woman retorted, staring at Seth's empty plate. He waved aside the platter thrust under his nose, and sat back to watch Angelina attempt to consume the food in front of her.

'The captain says we's eating well tonight,' Matty declared, 'and the folks from the village is invited to come up to the house after, if they have a mind—to drink your health. Caleb's going to kill a pig, and we're going to have the sweetest-tasting sucking-pig you've ever had in your life. Roasted over a fire outside, with my special sauces. You ain't tasted nothing 'til you've had my sauces. And sweet potatoes, chicken . . . ham, if you've a mind . . .'

'Oh, yes, Matty,' Angelina breathed, forgetting her eggs in her excitement, until the woman frowned at her and she began to eat again. 'The best of everything. Have we wines? Brandy?'

'Bless you, child, we have a cellar full of each . . . and rum. You leave it all to me . . . 'Cepting, of course, if you want to supervise, now you're mistress here?'

'I would not dream of it,' Angelina said quickly, knowing that she would deeply injure the Negress's feelings if she interfered with the preparations. 'But there is a chest in my bedroom with things for the house . . . plate and candlesticks. I want it all distributed, and the silver is to be used for the table tonight.'

'My men will be unloading the furniture I have brought when they return from the village,' Seth said, as Matty beamed with delight at the prospect of using all the fine things the captain had ignored for so long. It took a woman's touch, she mused, humming softly to herself as she waddled from the room. How this old place was going to change! And there would be children soon, if she was any judge of the captain's feelings for the beauty he had brought to his home. Fine strong boys for her to bounce on her knee in her old age . . . for Caleb to build toys for, to teach to ride as soon as they were old enough to stay in the saddle. Delicate little girls to grace the place alongside their beautiful mother.

'You have made Matty the happiest woman on earth,' Seth remarked, as Angelina pushed aside her plate with a soft sigh. She was not as hungry as she had thought —and far too excited to sit here doing nothing. 'I have not offered you my profound blessings and felicitations. Raven is a very lucky man.'

'Does he not deserve a little happiness after all he has been through?' she asked quietly. 'I shall do my utmost to make him forget the past.'

'I very much doubt if that will be possible, but perhaps . . .' The man lifted his shoulders with a rueful smile. 'If he has your love, he may in time relinquish all thought of ever returning to England to clear his name. Not that it would be possible now.'

'I do not understand you,' Angelina frowned at him, sensing a hidden meaning behind his words.

'I am the bearer of gifts and good wishes, but also the most disturbing of news, which I could not bring myself to convey to either of you until this morning. I told Jason before he left the house, and I'm afraid I have caused him great pain and distress.'

'How, Lord Courtney?' Angelina whispered, an icy hand clutching at her heart. What could cause pain to the man she loved? He was invulnerable here.

'His brother is dead. His ship—or rather what was left of her—and the crew, limped into Port Royal as I was about to leave. Most of the men, including Edgar Sarandon, had been washed overboard in a terrible storm at sea. The same one that hit these islands, I suspect.'

'Dead?' Her voice was barely audible, and the large, green eyes widened with shock.

'I'm afraid so, my dear. I regret being the one to bring such tidings at such a time of celebrating for you both.'

'I—I am not upset . . . I have known for a long time that I did not love Edgar. I—I cared for him, a little —but not as I care for—love—his brother,' Angelina admitted truthfully. 'I hope you do not think badly of me for the way I feel? Since I met Raven, I have begun to suspect I never even knew the man I was to marry. If—If

I am to accept everything I have been told, then I certainly did not. Have you known the family a long time?' she ventured to ask.

'A good many years. Jason's father and I were friends before I came to live out here. I often stayed at their family home in Gloucestershire. A beautiful spot. Jason loved that place so much . . .'

'Is he—do you . . .' She balked at an outright question, but as Seth looked at her across the table, she took all her courage in her hands and said, 'Do you believe him capable of such a monstrous crime?'

'No.'

'You sound so sure.'

'And you are not? It is a strange love you bear him,' came the grave answer, and she flushed at the criticism underlying his tone.

'I love him with all my heart. I would not do anything to hurt him . . . but I have been plucked from all I know, my friends and home, brought here to be his wife. Had I not fallen in love with him, he would still have married me, and kept me here against my will. That is the kind of man he is now. I have seen him fight—and kill a man in defence of me . . . I never want to see again the look in his eyes that I saw that night. He was like a man possessed. I never knew him before . . . But the man I saw then *was* capable of taking another human life—and did!'

'He was, and still is, a man of honour,' Seth told her, his voice growing more gentle as he came to understand the terrible conflict which raged inside her. 'He told me he did not kill poor Drusilla, and I believe him. He told me many things the night before he left England, and swore me to secrecy. I cannot break my pledge of silence—much as I dearly want to, so that your heart may be eased from the burden you carry.'

'No one was there—no one can verify his story, whatever it is . . . He will not discuss it with me. All I know from Edgar is that he saw Jason coming from the girl's room on the night she was killed. They fought, and the servants refused to detain Jason when he beat his brother and fled the house. Out of fear—or love, Lord Courtney?'

'Even as Raven, the man commands respect and awakens love in the most unexpected places, does he not?' Seth replied. 'He is the most honourable man I have ever met. You, yourself, can vouch for that.'

'How so?'

'You were on board the *Sea Witch* for some considerable time. Were you abused? Did he allow the crew to make themselves unpleasant to you? Were you molested in any way?'

'No—but . . .' How could she tell him how Raven's attentions to her had caused such distress in those first weeks . . . and now were so much desired, every minute of the day?

'The answer must be yes—or no,' he insisted with a frown.

'Well . . . No. But he is still a pirate. He has been attacking his brother's ships,' she declared.

'*His* ships, Miss Blackthorne. If, as I believe, he is innocent of any crime, he is still Lord Sarandon. Those ships which his brother acquired have never belonged to him. Jason began the business from a single vessel, just as he has done out here, and built it into a profitable concern. You have much in common. You have both worked hard to realise a dream. His brother, during that time, squandered his money in easy living, excessive drinking and gambling, not to mention an assortment of women that sent his poor father to his grave long before his time. Edgar hated Jason's successes—he always did everything so well.'

She had felt so sorry for Edgar when he told her the same thing, but now Angelina felt nothing. The news had still numbed her, and the implications were beginning to thrust themselves to the forefront of her mind.

'What was Edgar doing in these waters?'

Seth smiled at her, visualising her for a moment on board the *White Swan* as Jason had described her, in the garb of a cabin-boy, standing before him, threatening his life with a pistol. And she had used it! He marvelled at the strength, the courage and fortitude she had shown in achieving her aims in a world that ridiculed a woman with brains and the strength to assert her authority. What a pair they would make! And as for their children! The Caribbean would never be the same again!

'Actually he was looking for you. That was the story he told everyone before he fled for his life . . . He was in some duel or other over a woman—a married woman he has been associating with for some months. Her husband took offence when he made the liaison public news at a drunken party, and challenged him. Edgar never could take to a sword . . . he preferred pistols. As I heard it from one of the crew who survived, he ran the man through from behind. Of course that was unforgivable, and made his position not only intolerable—but precarious. The man has two brothers, I believe, who both sought to take his life. Edgar made the first available ship ready and left England the day after . . . and escaped not only arrest for murder, but a pack of creditors who have been hounding him since you left on your second voyage. He was penniless. He has disposed of all his assets; even the ships you gave him as a wedding gift were sold to pay off some of the debts, but they were insufficient. At sea they encountered the *White Swan* on her homeward journey, and I gather Jason gave the captain a message for his brother. The crewman said he was drunk for four days afterwards . . . and in such a foul mood that no one could go near him. Like a madman, was his description . . . All he talked about was killing his brother.'

'So he was not coming for me . . .' Angelina murmured. It helped to disperse the guilt she felt, small though it was, over his death. 'I—I gave him no ships, Lord Courtney. I would have done so on our wedding day . . . I left papers to that effect, but I *signed* nothing.'

'In his care, of course?' She nodded. 'It would have been an easy thing to forge your signature. Villains skilled in that art can be bought for a sixpence in some parts of London. I'm very much afraid you have nothing to go home to, my dear. He took everything. Like Jason, you have been deprived of what is rightfully yours. Edgar's death condemns him for ever to exile—this life he has chosen for himself on Eden.'

'And for me.' Never to return to England . . . never be able to challenge the accusation against him, to face his accusers and clear his name. The only witness to that nightmarish night was now dead. Charity still lived, but it would be a miracle if she ever recollected what had taken place. 'I shall make his life here worth while. He will never regret not being able to go home.'

No more would she. The choice had been made. How confident she sounded! Seth smiled again, and his hand covered hers across the table, but she sensed that he, too, had reservations. Nothing, but nothing, could replace what Jason had lost: his good name, and his honour; his home and friends; the business he himself had built from nothing. He had replaced it all—or tried to—with a way of life she now believed to be totally alien to his nature. He had substituted a Caribbean island for the majestic family home in Gloucestershire of which Charity had said he was so proud. His friends were not of his own kind, from his own background, but rough seamen, pirates, merchants—with only a few men of Seth Courtney's standing included, she suspected.

There was nothing she could do except to love him, and to show him with her love, her utter devotion, that she trusted him above all men and would stand by him no matter what difficulties lay ahead for them both. Tonight would be a start, she thought, as she rose and bade Seth excuse her, and hurried upstairs to find Charity. She needed all the help she could get to prepare the house for the forthcoming wedding *and* the special dinner tonight.

She was almost at the staircase when a man came out of one of the rooms along the passage. He reeled towards her as if drunk, and for a moment she thought that he was; she was opening her mouth to remonstrate with him when she saw the pistol coming up to menace her. As his head was lifted, she saw the wildness in the eyes which fastened on her, and heard as if in a dream, Edgar Sarandon snarl . . .

'No sound, Angelina . . . or I shall have to kill you too soon, and I do not want to do that. I want Jason to be here to see it . . . then him alongside you . . .'

She subsided against the wall, a hand creeping up to press against her breast where a diamond brooch glittered in the candlelight. Edgar's lips curled derisively at the sight of it.

'You—You . . . you went overboard,' she whispered, fighting down the panic threatening to render her incapable of movement or thought . . . Seth was still in the dining-room. If she screamed? But one look into the eyes of the man in front of her told her that she would not utter another sound. Was he mad? Had his terrible experience done this to him? She hardly recognised him. His clothes hung tattered and torn on his thin body. His skin had an unhealthy tinge to it . . . feverish . . . yet red and puffed in places. He had always looked so when he had been drinking for several days. Was that not what Seth had been told, that during the voyage from England he had been drinking incessantly? But the hand which held the pistol pointing at her was as steady as could be, and she was very afraid.

'I'm not a ghost. An avenging spirit come to claim what is mine, that's all. But I hear from the good Captain Forrester that you no longer consider yourself mine. You have given yourself to *him*! My brother! You damned bitch! Am I to be forever betrayed by fickle women? First her . . . now you . . . And you shall pay as she did for leading me on with your smiles and your sweet words . . . You'll be in hell before me, madam!'

'You are ill, Edgar . . . feverish!' Angelina's hand trembled as she extended it towards him. His smile grew as he saw her nervousness, and the chuckle which rose in his throat chilled her to the bone.

'That's what she said, too,' he murmured, leaning against the wall also, as if his strength was ebbing from him. 'Are you wondering how I came here? You must thank your kind captain for that. His ship picked me out of the water the day after I went overboard. I was half dead, but I had a goodly share of brandy inside me, and so perhaps that kept me alive in the water. They say the devil takes care of his own, don't they?'

Angelina darted a desperate glance towards the dining-room, but there was no sign of Seth, no sound from within. Perhaps he had gone out through the french windows for a walk, unaware of her perilous predicament. Edgar's words swam in her mind. He was going to wait for Jason's return before he killed her . . . and then his own brother. Hatred had driven him to the edge of madness! But it was his own fault that he had been driven from England penniless, probably with only the clothes on his back, deserted by friends and business acquaintances who shunned a man cowardly enough to run another through from behind. It was the most hideous of crimes!

'We are alone. The Negro woman and the man are busy out back trying to catch a pig, and I saw my brother leave as I came ashore. Too far away for me to put a ball in his back—regretfully.'

'You don't really mean to kill him! You can't! Why?' Angelina asked. She hoped he would not notice the way she was carefully edging along the wall away from him, but he did, and she froze as the pistol was cocked ominously.

'Be still or you die now!' Edgar threatened, and she obeyed, great desolation sweeping over her, for through the open door she could see into the dining-room. It was empty! She was alone. Alone with a man intent on killing her, taking, too, the life of the brother he hated for his successes in life. She knew he would pull the trigger to end her life without a qualm. She knew now that Jason was innocent of the accusation of murder. Here before her, surely, was the true culprit? Had he not said so? She had been so stunned by his appearance that she was only now beginning to recall what he had said, 'First her . . . now you . . . And you shall pay as she did . . .'

'You killed Drusilla Ansley and blamed your

brother,' she accused, and her voice was sharp with fear.

Edgar sketched a travesty of a bow in her direction, his pinched features derisive.

'I loved her, you know. Of course I loved even more the inheritance she would have come into upon her marriage . . . and Jason knew it, blast him. He turned her against me. She liked me once . . . loved me . . .'

His head jerked up suddenly in an attitude of intense concentration. Angelina stifled a cry as he stepped closer. She could hear voices now from outside . . . Matty singing and scolding Caleb alternately for failing to catch the sucking-pig for dinner. Her tones reverberated round the patio outside. They were coming closer. She was coming in, Angelina realised, horrified. Edgar might panic, and harm her . . .

'No!' With all her strength she grabbed at the hand clutching the pistol, coupled his wrist with her long fingers as he recovered and swung it back to menace her, and hung on like grim death. He swore at her viciously and cuffed her across the face with his free hand, but she refused to relinquish her hold. A scream of warning broke from her lips. She was unaware that she called out not only Matty's name, but Jason's . . . over and over again as she sank to her knees, half senseless from the blows rained on her face and body with his clenched fist. He was smiling as her head fell back and she slid to the floor. He was enjoying it! He was an animal! Drusilla would have stood no chance against him, for Angelina recalled how Charity had told her that she was a delicate girl. No more would she . . . For, despite his small frame, Edgar's strength was unbelievable. The eyes which stared down at her glowed like coals of fire as he levelled the pistol at her inert form.

He said in a voice shaking with rage, 'I think I shall kill

you now, and let him find you . . . That's how I meant it
to be last time, but he came too soon . . . I didn't know
the little fool had sent for him . . . She was afraid of me,
you see. When I want something, I reach out and take it.
Jason and I are alike in that respect—and I wanted
her . . .' He threw back his head, and laughed at the
horror registering on Angelina's face. 'You thought it
was him, didn't you? They all did . . . I made them think
it was like that. When he caught me coming away from
her room, I had to fight him . . . but even though he beat
me, I still won. I cried out to the servants that he had
attacked Drusilla, and killed her in her own bed. He
couldn't prove otherwise, for Charity's memory
vanished when I knocked her out of my way. Stupid old
woman to try to stop *me*.'

'*Jason* will stop you . . .' Angelina whispered. She
would not be alive to see it . . .

A shadow moved on the staircase. From behind one of
the tall pillars which lined the inlaid marble stairs, a
woman emerged. She, too, held a pistol, so large and
cumbersome that it was necessary for her to grip it with
both hands to take steady aim. Angelina's eyes widened
in disbelief, involuntarily betraying her presence to
Edgar.

He turned . . . saw her . . . For an instant he was too
taken aback with shock to react and, in that moment of
hesitation, Charity shot him through the chest. As
Angelina struggled to hold on to her fading senses, she
heard the woman say quite clearly and distinctly,

'I could not let it happen again, could I?'

And then, with Edgar's body sprawled across her, the
sightless eyes staring into hers, Angelina faded into
merciful oblivion.

*   *   *

'Are you sure you are all right?' Raven demanded for the third time, as he took Angelina by the shoulders and gazed long and hard into her face. A little colour had returned to it, for she had been sitting at Charity's bedside until the woman fell into a drugged sleep, with the aid of one of Matty's special potions, and had had a chance to compose herself to some degree. Two hours had passed since he had sprung from his hiding-place in the dining-room to tackle his brother, only to find that Charity's shot had deprived him of his revenge. Until he bent over Angelina and laid a hand over her heart, he was convinced she was dead, so still and lifeless did she look. Her loose hair was spread about her shoulders like tongues of fire, her eyes tightly closed, and there was blood on her gown. 'Come and sit down. I'll bring us each a drink.'

Wearily she sank on to the cushioned sofa before the fireplace and watched him cross to the decanters. He returned with two glasses well filled with rum.

She had come out of her faint to find herself surrounded by anxious faces. Seth and Caleb, Matty and most of the crew from the *White Swan*, whom John Forrester had led up to the house, worried about the state of Edgar Sarandon's mind. He had been raving for four days, and he did not like it. He was dangerous! He had been ordered to stay on board and prepare to sail again immediately. Instead, he had sent a man in all haste to the village in the wake of Jason, to fetch him back—with reinforcements. Thank heaven he had, she thought gratefully.

Jason had come in through the dining-room with Seth and the men hard on his heels, had reached the door, when he heard a shot . . . and sprang out to find

Angelina lying on the floor, his brother's body covering her.

In his blind rage, his fear, he thought she was dead, killed by the very man who four years before had taken the life of his ward. He had ravished an innocent girl because she repulsed his advances, then killed her in a mad rage to silence her for ever. He had been like a devil as he leapt upon his brother, dragging him away from Angelina's prostrate form . . . dragging him to his feet by the front of his blood-soaked shirt . . . Not until Seth had caught his arm and the murderous red haze before his eyes diminished, did he understand what was being said to him.

'He is dead, my boy. Dead! He cannot harm you any longer. Or her. Let him go, Jason! Let him go!'

Charity still stood like a silent statue on the stairs. The pistol had fallen from her numb fingers and lay at her feet. One of the crew retrieved it, and brought it to him. As he looked into her eyes, before Matty gently guided her back to her room, he knew that her memory had returned. The shock of seeing Angelina about to die had revived the nightmare of that night. It was not Angelina, but Drusilla she had seen, the life being choked from her young body after Edgar's drunken possession of her.

Now he, too, was dead! He had been spared the revenge he had sought for himself all these years, and in a way he was relieved, and yet angered. He had so many wrongs to right, and he had not been given the chance to do so . . .

'Is it over for you?' Angelina asked. He lifted the glass to her lips and made her drink the contents . . . as he had done once before when they spent the night in Tortuga, she remembered, and her cheeks flamed with colour as he bent and laid his lips against her cheek.

'Forever, my love. I am free now.'

'But . . . you are still a . . . fugitive,' she breathed.

'No . . . Not if I choose otherwise. Seth will accompany us back to England in a month or two, to clear my name. I must retrieve all your stolen property. He overheard everything, as did most of his crew. And there is Charity, remember . . . She can tell the truth as it happened. She said something about an onyx box—a wedding present. If she had not wanted to bring it to you, she would never have seen what was going on. When everything that was once mine has been restored to me, you shall have my name. That is as it should be. Lady Sarandon . . . It suits you!' His lips ventured further to the smooth hollow of her throat. 'Once and for all I shall be cleared of the charge of murder. It was Edgar who struck Drusilla down. Charity can confirm too that she was in love with someone else . . . Someone to whom she had not confided her feelings . . . Edgar's love for Drusilla was becoming an obsession, it terrified her, and so I suggested that we allow him to believe that it was me she was fond of. It was a small thing. I cared for the child as if she was my own sister. Can you understand that?'

Mutely Angelina nodded. How blind and stupid she had been not to see through Edgar's subterfuge. Yet she had not been the only one to be taken in.

'Are you sure you are all right?' Jason demanded yet again, taking her glass and setting it aside. He slipped an arm round her shoulders and drew her close to him. He could feel her trembling, and his mouth tightened visibly. 'He is dead, my angel. He cannot harm us now.'

'He—He was like a different person,' she whispered, turning her face up to his. His heart almost stopped beating as he saw the anguish mirrored in the depths of those green pools. 'I felt as if I had never known him.'

'I don't think you ever did. I wonder now if anyone did. We were never close, but we were so different in temperament that I gave it little thought. I had my way of life, and he his. That was it. He was unsuitable as a husband for Drusilla and I forbade the marriage, never dreaming what it would lead to when I pretended to love her as a future husband. After her death, of course, Edgar had all the weapons he needed at his disposal. My own admission that I cared . . . He put it about that she had repulsed me and that in a fit of rage I had raped and then killed her. I have a temper, as you well know. I am capable of . . . taking another life,' he reminded her quietly, and a new light glistened in her eyes as she looked up into his distraught features.

'For me. You killed for me . . . Do you think I shall ever forget that night? I would have given myself to you then, had you asked it of me.'

'And never been sure if I truly cared for you? No, that is not my way, and you should know that by now . . . In four years I have learned great patience, even though it greatly pains me now to exercise it.'

She blushed, understanding his meaning, and he, with a soft laugh, bent his head and laid his lips against the soft curving rise of her breast.

'Am I not the most docile of pirates? Where else would you find yourself such a patient lover?'

Angelina drew back from him with a mischievous smile. The past hours slipped to the back of her mind as she saw the gleam in those grey eyes and felt the strength of the hands caressing her body.

'Who will you be on our wedding night? Raven, the pirate? Jason, Lord Sarandon? Or just a man—my husband? There is nothing to choose between any of you, you know. I love them all dearly.'

Jason's smile was wicked as his face came close to hers, and his hands slipped beneath her robe. She had changed out of the violet silk which had been stained with Edgar's blood, horrified on seeing it at the shock he must have received when first he came upon her.

'Fickle creature! I can see I shall have my hands full with a woman who loves three men at the same time. As Raven, I shall carry you to my bedchamber in true pirate fashion. There, Jason will charm you, with all the manners and fine words befitting a gentleman, into divesting yourself of your very alluring bridal gown. And then your husband will show you how much he loves you . . . worships you . . . treasures you above all. What do you say to that, my love?'

Angelina had no chance to reply, for his mouth was on hers again, parting it, rousing the fire in her. And so she gave him a silent answer as her hands locked behind his dark head. An answer far more satisfying and promising to them both than any given word.

Matty paused in the doorway and looked at the tray of cold food she had prepared. The special dinner had been set aside for the wedding feast the next day, and everyone had gone back about their business in order to have things ready for the celebrations. She shrugged her shoulders and turned away, glancing back once more at the two figures entwined in each other's arms and totally oblivious of her presence . . . and went away humming to herself. It took a woman's touch in all things, sure enough! This old house would never be the same again . . . nor the captain, neither!